Cycling STRONGER

Cycling STRONGER

Edmund R. Burke, Ph.D.
Harvey Newton, M.A.

Book design and illustration: Rick Joyner
Editing: Linda Belans

The information and ideas in this book are for educational and instructional purposes and are not intended as prescriptive advice. Consult your physician before starting any exercise or weight loss program.

Performance Inc.
One Performance Way
Chapel Hill, NC 27514

Printed in the United States of America

Acknowledgments

We would like to thank Performance, Inc. for seeing the need to produce a book about off-season and resistance training for cyclists. To Karen Homa: without her support, encouragement, and, when necessary, prodding, we never would have finished this book. Thanks also to Richard Snook and Clark Brace for an excellent preliminary editing job and astute suggestions. Finally, special thanks to Steve Penny, Media Director of the United States Cycling Federation, and to the athletes from the United States Cycling Team who gave their time for the photo sessions (Carl Sundquist not pictured):

Eve Stephenson

- 1992 World Championships: 1st, Team Time Trial
- 1992 National Championships:
  1st, Team Time Trial
  4th, Individual Time Trial
  6th, Olympic Selection Road Race
  10th, Criterium
  14th, Individual Road Race
- 1991 World Championships: 4th, Team Time Trial
- 1991 National Championships: 2nd Individual Time Trial

Dirk Copeland

- 1992 Barcelona Olympic Games: 9th, Team Pursuit
- 1992 Olympic Track Trials:
  1st, Team Pursuit
  6th, Individual Pursuit
- 1992 Collegiate Track Nationals:
  1st, Omnium
  1st, Kilometer Time Trial
  1st, Individual Pursuit
- 1991 Pan American Games: Silver Medalist

Matt Hamon

- 1992 Barcelona Olympic Games: 9th, Team Pursuit
- 1992 Olympic Track Trials:
  1st, Team Pursuit
  2nd, Individual Pursuit
  3rd, Points Race
- 1991 Pan American Games: Silver Medalist, Team Pursuit

Foreword from the Authors

The purpose of this book is to introduce you to the extraordinary world of indoor training and, thereby, improve your cycling performance. Cycling Stronger will acquaint you with information to construct an indoor fitness program tailored to your particular needs and interests.

The preparation of Cycling Stronger was an exciting challenge for us. When approached by Performance, Inc. to produce the book, we called upon our years of experience working with athletes to try to put together the best book on resistance and indoor training for the cycling enthusiast. We have written Cycling Stronger for those who are contemplating a first-time investment in indoor equipment, as well as those who already know something about such devices, but need a useful handbook for setting up a comprehensive program.

This book offers you easy-to-follow guidelines for designing your yearly indoor fitness program. These guidelines, based on the same sound principles of training we use with athletes on the United States Cycling Team, are appropriate for adults, children and adolescents — the whole family can participate. We have also included detailed instructions and illustrations on how to use the various pieces of equipment.

As you read Cycling Stronger, you should keep in mind that becoming knowledgeable about indoor training is only one of the essential ingredients in your personal recipe for sensible exercise. If you want to make your indoor exercise experience as productive and enjoyable as possible, we suggest that you take several steps. The most critical step is that you make an unwavering commitment to exercise on a regular basis. For most individuals, that commitment will be based, at least in part, on an understanding that regular aerobic exercise and strength training makes sense for almost everyone, and that exercise truly has medicinal properties.

Congratulations on having accomplished a major step toward a balanced fitness program by investing in Performance home fitness equipment. Follow these guidelines and recommendations and you'll realize the connection among balanced fitness, improved cycling performance and quality of life.

Explore Cycling Stronger. Read it in bits. And good luck as you begin using the equipment featured in this book in your balanced fitness program.

Edmund R. Burke, Ph.D. and Harvey Newton, M.A.
Colorado Springs, Colorado

Contents

Introduction *1*
Chapter 1, Cycling Stronger *5*
  Strength, Power and Endurance *5*
  Anaerobic Energy System *6*
  Aerobic Energy System *7*
  Fitness Guidelines *7*
  Resistance Training *7*
  Aerobic Training *8*
  Training Effect *8*
  Summary *9*
Chapter 2, Resistance Training *11*
  Strength Training for Improved Aerobic Performance *11*
  Injury Prevention *12*
  Muscle Size *13*
  Terminology *13*
  Number of Reps *13*
  Periodization *14*
  Transition Phase *15*
  Foundation Phase *16*
  Strength Phase *16*
  Power Phase *16*
  Peaking or Maintenance Phase *17*
  Training Tips *17*
  Summary *18*
Chapter 3, Resistance Training Exercises *21*
  Upper Body Pushing *21*
  Upper Body Pulling *25*
  Lower Back *29*
  Abdominals *32*
  Lower Body *34*
  Supplemental or Specialty Exercises *41*
  Workouts *48*
  Progressive Resistance *48*
  Workout Tips *49*
  Injury Prevention *49*
  Weight Training Safety Tips *50*
  Summary *50*
Chapter 4, Aerobic Training *53*
  Heart Rate *53*
  Finding Your Training Zone *54*
  Fat Burning Zone *55*

Target Heart Rate Zone *55*
Anaerobic Zone *55*
Exercise & Caloric Cost *56*
Training Tips *57*
Summary *58*
Chapter 5, Rowing and Stepping *61*
Rowing Indoors *61*
The Stroke *62*
Workouts *64*
Injury Prevention *64*
Stair Climbing *65*
The Step *65*
Workouts *66*
Injury Prevention *67*
Summary *67*
Chapter 6, Spinning Your Wheels Indoors *69*
Rollers *69*
Wind vs. Magnetic Trainers *70*
Spinning *72*
Workouts *72*
Injury Prevention *75*
Summary *75*
Chapter 7, Stretching *77*
The Stretch *77*
Stretch Exercises *77*
Summary *83*
Suggested Reading *84*
Videotape *84*

Introduction

All summer and fall you worked hard on your bike and had good results. Now it's the off-season and you want a little rest. Put the bike in storage and take it out again in the spring. Right? Wrong.

After a short break, which is necessary for your body to recover, think about adding some cross-training activities to your program, like stair stepping, rowing and resistance training (working your muscles against a resisting force to maintain strength and endurance). The whole idea behind off-season training is to integrate other activities into your cycling skills - activities that will increase your strength, power and endurance. It's a great feeling to get back on your bike in the spring with your fitness intact from last season.

Most of us have very busy schedules and staying in shape requires extreme efficiency. These three words, "efficiency of effort," form the core for creating your own home fitness program. Efficiency of effort, producing maximum gains with minimal time spent, is the goal for most of us when designing our off-season training program. In addition, due to weather conditions and short winter days, there's no better place to accomplish off-season training than in your own home.

You can make great strides with an indoor training program. Just ask cyclists like Greg LeMond, Davis Phinney and members of the US Cycling Team who have established training centers in their own homes. They enjoy working out at home because it gives them time to concentrate on specific exercises to improve their cycling performance.

The bottom line is, you must be creative and innovative to get the best results. With Cycling Stronger and your own creativity, a great workout is only a few moments away; a different grip on the multi-gym, a varied stepping rhythm on the stepper, a new intensity on the stationary wind-load simulator, or a more rapid stroke rate on the rower. By varying your workouts you'll create maximum gains in the shortest amount of time .

Your home equipment will allow you to reach your fitness goals and prepare properly for the upcoming cycling season. Anyone who is serious about cycling, or for that matter just improving overall fitness, should have a few basic pieces of equipment. It makes no difference if you are a competitive athlete or just trying to tone your muscles; the home fitness center is the most efficient way to help you reach your physical potential.

Chapter 1 Cycling Stronger

Strength, Power and Endurance

Successful performance in cycling requires a combination of muscular strength, power and endurance. Strength is the ability to overcome an external force (such as your foot against a pedal); whereas, power is the ability to overcome the external force in the shortest amount of time. Both of these components stress the anaerobic energy system which is not dependent on oxygen. Endurance, the ability to sustain an activity over a long period of time, stresses your aerobic energy system which is dependent on oxygen.

When you work your muscles intensively for short periods of time (such as lifting weights or sprinting), you stress your anaerobic energy system. Working your muscles aerobically stresses your muscles over a long period of time which will improve your aerobic capacity. But to be successful at most sports, you need a strong combination of both energy systems.

The particular event an athlete trains for within cycling determines which of

these components should be emphasized. Road racing, for example, requires mostly muscular endurance, but power is also needed to climb steep hills and sprint for the finish line. The same holds true for touring. You need endurance to cover long miles on a day-to-day basis and strength to carry your gear in panniers. The match sprint depends primarily on strength and power for an explosive sprint, though endurance is important for the long training days. Most people train adequately for the endurance component but not for the strength and power components. Therefore, resistance training should also be part of a complete training program.

Anaerobic Energy System

A physiological measure that relates closely to the anaerobic energy system is the lactate or anaerobic threshold. This threshold occurs at a point during exercise when the majority of energy is derived from anaerobic sources. As a result, there is a large rise in lactic acid in the blood, a product of anaerobic metabolism.

Your body is designed to tolerate only a certain amount of stress. When exercising at a comfortable pace, you don't produce a significant amount of lactic acid. But as soon as you start exercising at a pace that feels hard (such as sprinting), lactic acid starts to build up and you feel fatigued. This prevents you from over-stressing your body.

Lactate threshold is not pre-determined and with training, you can improve it. Interval training (repeated intervals of very hard exercise followed by exercising at an easy pace) is a common method used to improve the lactate threshold breakpoint. There is also scientific evidence suggesting that strength training may improve the lactate threshold. With an improved threshold you can perform more work before fatigue sets in, which means you can do one more sprint or climb a hill in a harder gear.

Aerobic Energy System

A physiological measure of your endurance is maximal oxygen consumption or maximum aerobic capacity (VO_2 max). Simply stated, it's a measure of the amount of oxygen your body uses during a maximal bout of exercise. Consider for a moment that your body is like an automobile engine, with your heart and lungs pumping the fuel throughout your body. Your VO_2 max represents your engine capacity, so having a high VO_2 max is like having a powerful engine.

VO_2 max is strongly related to exercise performance. Endurance athletes usually have high aerobic capacities that allow them to compete successfully in their events. The higher your aerobic capacity, the more comfortable you will be when exercising at a given workload. For example, if your VO_2 max is 50 ml/kg/min (milliliters of oxygen used per kilogram of body weight per minute), and your friend's is 40 ml/kg/min, who do you think will hurt more if you are both cycling at 35 ml/kg/min? You will probably find the ride easier, because you will be working at a lower percentage of your VO_2 max.

Fitness Guidelines

Many people beginning a fitness program still think "no pain, no gain." They usually think they have to cycle until they are over-tired and their bodies ache. This idea is outdated. By using proper guidelines, the initial tiredness or soreness will be replaced shortly by an increased energy level for work and recreation and an increased sense of well-being.

Since 1978 the American College of Sports Medicine (ACSM) has influenced the medical and scientific communities with its position-statement on "The Recommended Quantity and Quality of Exercise for Developing and Maintaining Fitness in Healthy Adults." But recently, the ACSM revised its recommendations, expanding and revising advice on cardio-respiratory fitness and body composition. They now recommend adding resistance training. This is new information to those of us who only cycle, run, swim, watch our body weight, and control our diet in an attempt to maintain fitness.

Resistance Training

The ACSM recognizes the increasing importance of maintaining strength as a health benefit as we get older. The rationale for adding of strength training to the guidelines is a result of a ten year follow-up study on masters runners. Those who continued to train aerobically without upper body exercise, maintained their VO_2 max over the years, but lost about 4.5 pounds of lean body mass. Those, however, who included strength training in their program, maintained lean body mass along with their aerobic capacity 10 years later.

Research also shows that consistent resistance training helps maintain bone and muscle mass as we get older. For women, strength training (along with the aerobic work) may also protect against post-menopausal bone loss and osteoporosis.

The guidelines recommend that two strength-training sessions per week should be added to a workout schedule. We recommend three sessions a week during the off-season and two days a week for maintenance during the in-season.

The new ACSM guidelines recommend a minimum of 1 set of 8 to 12 repetitions of 8 to 10 strength exercises of your major muscle groups per session. A complete detailed strength training program will be outlined in a later section of this book. If weights or other resistance training devices are not available, add calisthenics to your program.

Aerobic Training

The new ACSM statement, published in 1991, reiterates the four initial recommendations on duration, intensity, frequency and various modes of aerobic activity, with slight changes. The duration is now 20 to 60 minutes, versus a minimum of 15 minutes.

Intensity of exercise can be determined by 2 methods. The first is the familiar use of target heart rate. The guidelines state that you should aim to work at 60 to 90% of your maximum heart rate (max HR), (max HR = 220 - your age). The second method is to train at 50 to 85% of your VO_2 max (determined by doing a stress test on a bicycle ergometer at a medical facility).

Duration is dependent upon the intensity of the activity; those who like to work at a lower intensity should work out longer. Low to moderate intensity cycling is best for most adults, because higher intensity workouts can increase the risk of injury. Beginners can achieve a significant gains from low intensity workouts. If you're already fit and want to improve, gradually increase your intensity.

Again, the type of activity should include anything that uses large muscle groups and is rhythmical and aerobic in nature, such as cycling. Other activities could include stair stepping, cross-country skiing, hiking, rowing, swimming, etc. These activities need to be carried out 3 to 5 days per week.

Training Effect

Duration, intensity and frequency of training stimulate what is known as the aerobic training effect. Any training done below ACSM guidelines will not be sufficient enough to produce that effect. Conversely, exercising more than the recommended amount does not significantly increase the aerobic training effect, although athletes training for competition need to exercise more. It is important to remember not to overdo it; your body needs adequate recovery from a hard workout. Keep in mind that ACSM recommendations are guidelines for the average person, not Greg LeMond training for the Tour de France. In general, endurance training for fewer than 2 days per week at less than 60% of max HR for fewer than 20 minutes per day, without a well-rounded resistance and flexibility program, is inadequate for developing and maintaining fitness in healthy adults.

An appropriate warm-up and cool-down, including flexibility exercises, is also recommended. While many of us will need to train with more mileage and at a greater intensity to race competitively or ride a Century, it is important to remember that if most people follow ACSM guidelines they will achieve increased physical and health benefits at the lowest risk. Below is a table outlining the guidelines:

	Strength Training	*Aerobic Exercise*	*Stretching*
Frequency	*2 to 3 sessions/week*	*3 to 5 sessions/week*	*3 to 6 sessions/week*
Intensity	*8-12 reps until fatigued*	*60-90% of max HR*	*"easy feeling stretch"*
Time	*20-40 minutes*	*20-60 minutes*	*10 minutes*
Type	*10 exercises*	*any rhythmical activity*	*10 stretches*

Summary

Following ACSM guidelines can result in permanent lifestyle changes for most Americans. The good news is, with the right approach, exercise can and should be pleasant. You can combine strength training, cycling and flexibility activities that you enjoy while gaining valuable health benefits. Cross-training is also an effective way to improve your cycling skills. It is important to loosen up on your training schedule and experience other exercise schedules to prevent you from getting stale. Your home equipment can help you maintain or improve your fitness.

Chapter 2 Resistance Training

Resistance training has many benefits that can improve your athletic performance and overall health. In the previous chapter, we offered a few benefits suggested by the American College of Sports Medicine. But perhaps the most important is reflected in the well-known saying, "If you don't use it, you lose it." To maintain your lean body mass as you age requires strength training. In addition to maintaining muscle mass and increasing strength and power, strength training also offers benefits that are extremely important for any endurance athlete — improved aerobic performance and injury prevention.

Strength Training for Improved Aerobic Performance

Recently, interest in strength training has increased among middle and distance athletes in many sports. Many want to know if strength training and aerobic conditioning are compatible during the same periods.Will strength training provide the strength, power, suppleness, stamina and potential for speed that other athletes will not develop unless they work equally hard? It may seem inconsistant that strength training, which predominantly uses the anaerobic energy system, can improve cycling, which primarily uses the aerobic energy system. Recent research, however, supports this notion. When exercising aerobically at a comfortable pace you use both energy systems, but primarily the aerobic energy system. When you push the pace or as you come toward the end of your workout, your anaerobic energy system becomes more important. If it is in shape from strength training, you will be able to perform more work before you become fatigued.

It has only been within the last few years that researchers and coaches have begun to investigate these issues. Several recently published studies have shown that strength training can increase strength and time-to-exhaustion. These increases were an interesting finding, especially for athletes looking for that edge to improve their performance. Researchers also examined VO_2 max, but no improvements were expected or observed since this type of exercise does not stress the aerobic energy system.

A study in the late 1980's investigated the impact of adding heavy resistance-training to increase leg strength in eight runners and cyclists who had been training for several years. Strength training was performed for three days per week for 10 weeks, while all athletes continued their normal endurance training. At the end of the 10 weeks, running time-to-exhaustion, at maximal work rates, was increased by 13% for the runners and 11% for the cyclists. Leg strength was increased by an average of 30%, with no increase in VO_2 max. Overall, the athletes were able to exercise longer before they felt fatigued, most likely a result of their resistance training.

The data did not demonstrate any negative performance effects of adding heavy-resistance training to ongoing endurance training programs. The study showed that certain types of endurance performance, particularly those requiring fast-twitch fiber recruitment (power muscle fiber), can be improved by strength training supplementation.

Recently, a group of researchers from the University of Maryland, completed a study investigating the effects of strength training on lactate threshold and endurance performance. Eighteen healthy males were randomly assigned either to a strength training group or a control group (a standard of comparison for verifying or checking the results of a research study) for 12 weeks of training. There were no changes in aerobic capacity after the 12 weeks, but the group that participated in strength training showed a 33% increase in cycling time-to-exhaustion at 75% of aerobic capacity. The strength-training group was able to perform more work before fatigue set in.

There was also a significant reduction in plasma lactate concentrations at all relative exercise intensities between 55 and 75% of aerobic capacity. Less lactic acid most likely means that the anaerobic energy system became more efficient through strength training. This improved endurance performance was associated with a 12% increase in lactate threshold after 12 weeks of resistance training. This means that although two athletes have the same aerobic capacity, the one with a higher anaerobic threshold may be more successful.

Steve Fleck, Ph.D., sports physiologist in charge of strength training research in the Division of Sports Medicine at the Olympic Training Center in Colorado Springs, says, "A higher lactate threshold means that an athlete can ride at a higher intensity before fatigue sets in and causes a reduction in cycling speed. Their [University of Maryland researchers] findings indicate that strength training improves endurance performance independent of changes in oxygen consumption. This improvement appears to be related to increases in lactate threshold and increased leg strength." Simply stated, Dr. Fleck suggests that endurance and strength training are not mutually exclusive and that both may be needed for improved performance.

Injury Prevention

Resistance training will improve strength, power and overall aerobic performance. An additional benefit is that it offers injury prevention as well. Resistance training helps strengthen the muscles, tendons and ligaments around the foot, ankle, knee and hip joints. It can be used to correct muscle imbalances and help prevent stiffness, aches, pains and injury.

Total body muscle imbalance is common among cyclists who have strong legs and weak backs, shoulders, and arms. This imbalance can cause injury. The upper body needs strength training to balance out the strong legs. Resistance training can be translated into real advantages for any type of cyclist, advantages that can improve pedaling performance, endurance, and speed.

Muscle Size

While there is evidence that resistance training results in increased strength for cyclists, there are those who believe it will cause too much increase in muscle bulk (hypertrophy). Most arguments against the use of weights for cyclists center around the premise that they will become muscle bound and gain too much weight. Understandably, cyclists do not want to gain useless weight that will be carried like a lead water bottle up a hill. However, the type of program we have outlined in this book will actually help you climb and sprint more effectively.

Actual muscle growth is due to specific training and dietary regimens designed for that purpose. If you concentrate on strengthening muscles precisely for cycling, rather than becoming an Olympic-style weightlifter or body builder, no problems should occur. In addition, the amount of muscle you put on your body is also a function of heredity. Occasionally we have seen the "Terminator" road cyclist or the "Lean and Mean" sprinter, but generally, specific body types tend to seek certain events because of their immediate success in that sport.

Terminology

Before we discuss the details of resistance training, it is important that you become familiar with some of the basic terms used in strength training.

- Repetitions (Reps) - the number of times a weight is lifted consecutively.
- Set - a group of repetitions performed in sequence; a brief period of rest follows each set in order to recover.
- Volume - the total number of reps performed in a day, week, month or year.
- Load or Tonnage - the total amount of weight lifted in a day, week, month or year.
- Intensity - average weight lifted (load/reps = intensity).
- Repetition Maximum (RM) - the intensity associated with strength training is known as an RM. It is the weight you can handle for an assigned number of repetitions. For instance, a 10 RM weight in the Leg Curl might be 40 lbs. This means you can perform 10 reps, but you will fail to lift 40 lbs on the 11th rep. In another phase of training you might use a higher intensity (more weight) for a 6 RM. This might mean that 55 lbs equals your 6 RM.

Number of Reps

It is essential to understand both the benefits and logic behind how many reps you will perform. A different number of reps performed in a set will have a different result.

Performing 15 or more reps is associated with muscular endurance training. This number is helpful during the first few weeks of training, but should not be used for an extended period of time. Generally speaking, cyclists will benefit from muscular endurance training on the bike, and should use resistance training equipment for strengthening.

Reps in the range from 8 to 12 are normally associated with hypertrophy, or muscular growth, but performing reps in this range does not mean larger muscles. Such muscle growth is dependent on several factors, such as genetic potential, diet and the amount of exercise done. Cyclists, therefore, should not be concerned about having the muscle hypertrophy that is seen in body builders.

Strength gains occur more quickly when reps are in the range of 1 to 6. However, there is no need for a cyclist to be concerned with "maxing out" or performing 1, two, or three RM movements. Such high intensity attempts may lead to injury, especially for those who have just begun a strength training program.

Periodization

The real emphasis should be given to utilizing a proper resistance training program planned for cycling, especially if you want to see improvements in strength, power and endurance. Periodization (training differently for different results) is the missing link in most cycling-resistance training programs.

During the year of training on the bike, cyclists will work at different levels of exertion at different times. During early season rides, it is common to train in the small chain ring and to maintain a rapid cadence (90-100 rpm) at relatively slow speeds. However, if cyclists trained this way all year long, they would be unable to meet the demands of racing or other major events which require much larger gears, with frequent accelerations of pace, including sprinting. As a result, training gradually takes on more intense aspects, including hill training, intervals and sprints.

Resistance training parallels this closely. If a cyclist always trains at 10 or 15 reps, she will miss much of the strength benefit of resistance training, since strength comes from higher intensity, with fewer reps. A strength athlete performs 1 to 3 reps, whereas a cyclist should perform between four and six reps. Such high intensity training must occur only after a proper preparation of lifting lighter weights for higher repetitions.

Resistance training should also be varied over the year, just as cycling training. If this is your first year of strength training, concentrate on learning the proper technique of the exercises, and work in the 8 to 12 twelve repetition range. After the first year, plan to use the periodized approach described below.

There are five phases to the periodizing training program which will support your year round resistance training program. They are transition, foundation, strength, power and peaking or maintenance phases.

Transition Phase

The season is over, and you've taken a few weeks of "active rest," which means you put the bike away and have turned to other forms of aerobic training in order to maintain your fitness. This period is essential, since it helps prevent both physical and mental "burnout." The days are also shorter and colder, and you resign yourself to indoor training.

You should start your resistance training with the Transitional Phase, shifting the emphasis from cycling to strength training. The purpose is to prepare you for the higher intensity strength training which comes later. Just as you ease back into training on the bike or any type of aerobic exercise, you need to ease into strength training. The emphasis is on getting started correctly, without experiencing unnecessary muscle soreness.

In many cases, the exercises you choose may include your own body weight, rather than actually attempting strength training on a home gym. This could include push-ups, pull-ups, crunches, floor back extensions and lunges. If, however, you find upper body exercises, like push-ups and pull-ups to be too difficult to perform for the assigned number of reps, use a home gym such as the Performance RTS-30 to perform exercises which will work the same muscles in a similar fashion.

Follow one of two established training modes — circuit training or priority training. Circuit training means performing set one of Exercise A, then immediately going to set one of Exercise B, followed by set one of Exercise C, etc. until you have performed each movement. The exercise sequence should be varied, so that emphasis is not maintained in a particular part of the body, but the blood flow is constantly changing. Circuit training produces good cardio-respiratory benefits, so many cyclists like this form of exercise. However, because rest is minimal between exercises, and because exercises vary greatly, the standard benefits of resistance training (strength, power and muscular growth) are minimized. Circuits are recommended primarily for Transition workouts.

With priority training, you perform set one of Exercise A, rest one to two minutes, perform set two of Exercise A, rest one to two minutes, and perform set three of Exercise A. After this, rest and prepare for set one of Exercise B. This is the normally recommended form of resistance training. Remember to actually get off the exercise apparatus and move around between sets. Get a drink of water, record your workout in a training log or cheer on your training partner during this break. Then come back ready for another hard effort on your next set, unlike circuit training in which the rest is designed to be inadequate for another hard effort.

Repetitions of strength training exercises are in the 12 to 20 range during the Transitional Phase, with each exercise repeated from one to three sets (each set contains 12-20 reps). Resistance is light to moderate. This phase is similar to easy spinning, low-geared first attempt at outdoor winter riding. This phase usually lasts two to four weeks.

Foundation Phase

After this break-in period, training switches to the Foundation Phase in which high volume is the key. Weights are moderate, reps are 8 to 12 RM, and sets are usually between 3 and 5. This will be closer to the training used by a body builder, however, do not expect to see any massive muscles appear.

This phase is important because you are preparing your muscles for the hard work ahead. It is similar to long, slow, distance-mileage which occurs early in the season. In both cases, the volume is high and the intensity is moderate. This phase may last 4 to 12 weeks.

Strength Phase

The next step is the Strength Phase. Weights become heavier, reps are 4 to 6, and sets are usually between 5 and 7. Before heavy weights are lifted, it is essential to have a proper warm-up, performing the same movement first with a lighter weight.

This phase is similar to adding hill work to riding. If you begin with this phase before doing the Transitional and Foundation Phases, injury is more likely. However, by following the proper sequence of phases, your muscles will be prepared for this heavy load. This phase lasts from 4 to 8 weeks.

Power Phase

Strength by itself is fine, but to ensure success in your event you want explosive force. That brings us to the Power Phase, which also lasts at least 4 weeks, and perhaps as many as 12. Since it will be late winter/early spring, and you will be riding more, it is acceptable to cut back to two days per week for this phase. Weights and sets are reduced somewhat and reps are in the 6 to 15 range.

The main emphasis in the Power Phase is on speed of performing the movement. This phase is similar to the creation of power on the bike (sprinting and intervals). Power is an explosive strength, that allows you to move a heavy object very quickly. Hill climbing is generally not pure power, but strength and power-endurance. This concept is frequently misunderstood.

Increased power (a combination of speed and strength) is probably the most important result of resistance training. As in cycling, in order to become more powerful or explosive, this training is essential. During the Power Phase of resistance training, the actual lifting motion should be performed quickly, while the recovery should still be slow and controlled, as the other phases.

Peaking or Maintenance

Finally, you have arrived at the outdoor racing season. You must decide now whether or not to continue resistance training. Usually, it is wise to maintain some strength work, especially in body parts that do not receive much stress through cycling, like the abdominals, arms and back.

This is accomplished through the Peaking or Maintenance Phase. Two workouts each week, lasting between 20 and 30 minutes, will be sufficient. Circuit training may be followed, as this will work muscular endurance. It is important not to simply stop all resistance training so early that the benefits disappear by the time the big races or events arrive. A great deal of strength can be maintained with a minimal investment in training. Remember to taper your resistance training workouts from 7 to 10 days before a major event (race, century etc.) in order to emphasize cycling.

Year-round periodized training is a healthy and proper training regimen that will prepare you for any major event, or simply keep you fit and strong. Below is a chart outlining the five phases involved in periodized resistance training:

Periodized Resistance Training

Phase	*Benefit*	*days/wk*	*sets*	*reps*	*Weight*	*Length*
Transitional	*preparation*	*3*	*1-3*	*12-20*	*light to moderate*	*2-4 wks*
Foundation	*muscle growth*	*3*	*3-5*	*8-12*	*moderate*	*4-12 wks*
Strength	*get strong*	*3*	*5-7*	*4-6*	*heavy*	*4-8 wks*
Power	*explosive force*	*2-3*	*3-6*	*6-15*	*moderate with speed*	*4-12 wks*
Peaking	*maintain*	*2*	*1-2*	*4-8*	*moderate*	*cycling season*

Training Tips

Generally, it is recommended that you first perform exercises that use more than one body joint (multiple joint movements). Single joint movements, especially for the arms, are kept for the end of the workout.

Training small muscles and single joints first will cause fatigue which can interfere with the proper performance of the more complicated multiple joint movements during which you will handle more weight. For example, Bent-Over-Rowing, which includes both the shoulder and elbow joints, should be done before Arm Curls, which only involves the elbow joint only.

Only multiple-joint movements should be used during the Strength and Power Phases. This is a time when you will be handling heavier loads or performing quick movements. Doing this with only one joint could lead to injury.

Normally, workouts should occur three times per week, with one day of rest from resistance training between each workout. Monday-Wednesday-Friday is the traditional recommendation.

Summary

As you strengthen the muscles used to pedal the bicycle, you become a better cyclist. You can ride hills with greater authority, and ride the flats with greater endurance. And, most importantly, you will make the time you spend on your bicycle more enjoyable and comfortable.

Chapter 3 Resistance Training Exercises

Now that you have an understanding of how resistance training will proceed throughout the year, the following will describe the exercises in detail. One of the simplest ways to address strength training is to divide your workout into the following six categories:

- Upper Body Pushing
- Upper Body Pulling
- Lower Back
- Abdominals
- Lower Body
- Supplemental or Specialty Exercises

With the Performance RTS-30 or other similar home-gym equipment, you can perform exercises from each of these categories. If you decide to supplement your training with other resistance training exercises (using free weights or body weight), you can use the same categories.

Each strength training exercise describes how to position your body relative to the equipment (preparation). Preparation is followed by a description of the exercise movement pattern, how the exercise may directly benefit your cycling (cycling application), and finally, which muscles are involved. The exercise is repeated for the appropriate number of suggested reps in each set.

Upper Body Pushing Exercises

Upper body pushing exercises include some form of elbow extension (straightening of the elbow joint). We all know how fatigued we feel early in the season, especially after a long ride. This fatigue usually shows up in the hands, the triceps (the back of the upper arms), the trapezius muscles (upper back), and the neck muscles.

Upper body pushing may not help you propel your bike any faster, but it will help develop a well-rounded, total body strength that certainly can make cycling easier. Increased upper body strength is particularly important to those specializing in mountain bike riding which requires greater strength to control the bike. This is especially true for the majority of women cyclists who tend to have less upper body strength than men.

Recommended RTS-30 exercises include:

- Chest Press
- Triceps Press
- Triceps Pushdown

Chest Press

- Preparation: Release lock lever and fit roll pads to top hole for leg room if required.

- Description: From the seated position grip handles and push forward by extending the elbow. Keep shoulders and hips in place and do not arch the low back.

- Cycling Application: Upper body support while riding and overall balance of muscularity/strength.

- Muscles: Deltoids, triceps and pectorals.

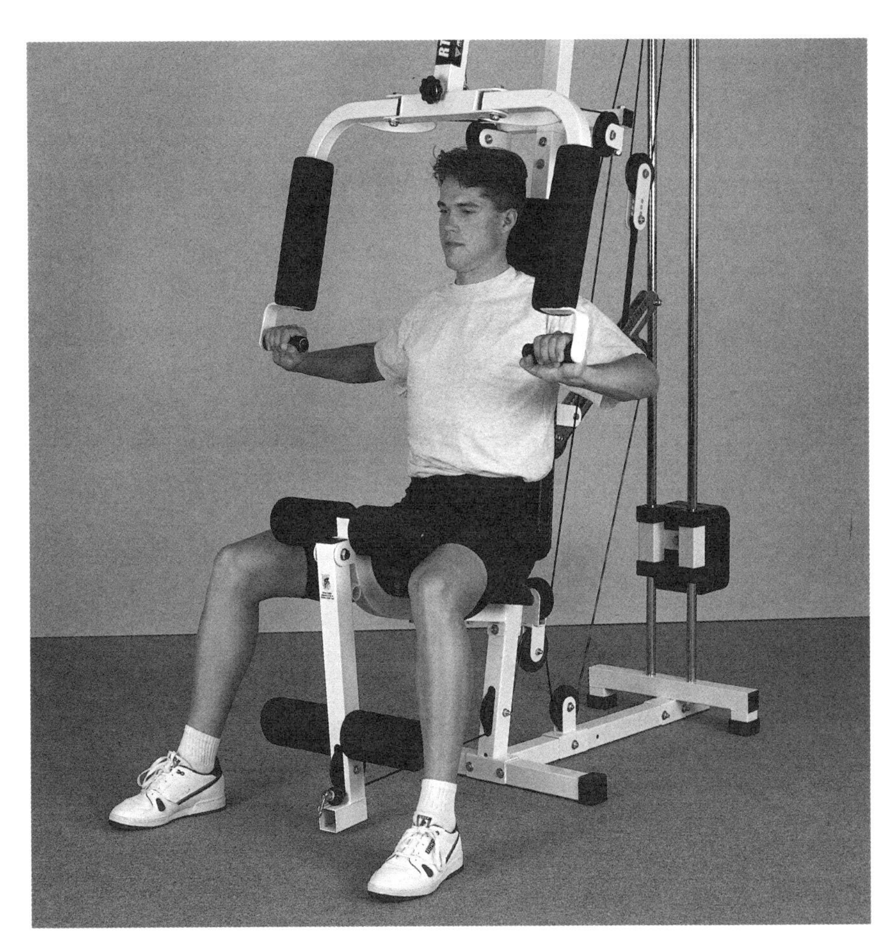

Triceps Press

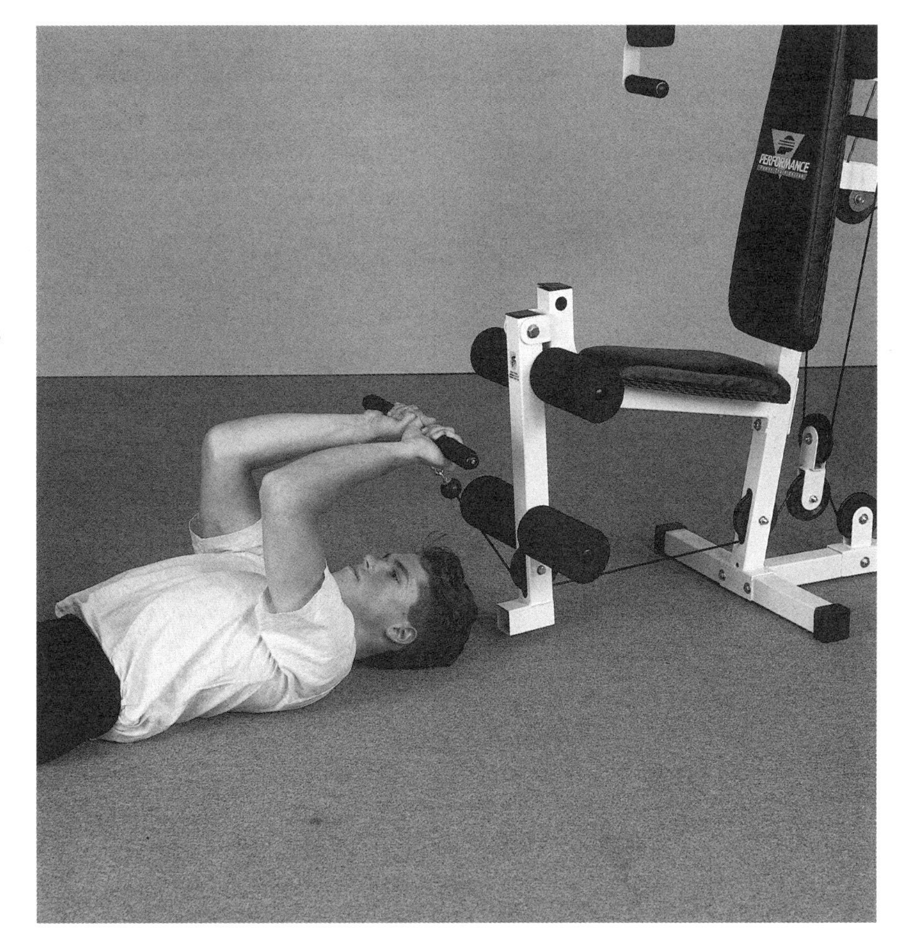

- Preparation: Fit t-bar to low pulley. Lie on your back with your head near the low pulley.

- Description: Use a narrow grip, with palms facing upward. Keep elbows close together and pointed upward. Bend and extend the elbow joint in a smooth motion. Completely straighten the arms at the top and allow the bar to come all the way down at the bottom.

- Cycling Application: Support upper body, especially while on handlebar drops.

- Muscles: Triceps.

Triceps Pushdown

- Preparation: Fit t-bar to high pulley. Adjust the chain to proper length.
- Description: Place hands about 3 inches apart, with palms facing downward. Keep elbows alongside torso throughout entire movement and straighten the elbow joint until arms are straight. Slowly return to starting position (elbow fully bent).
- Cycling Application: Support of upper body, especially while on handlebar drops.
- Muscles: Triceps.

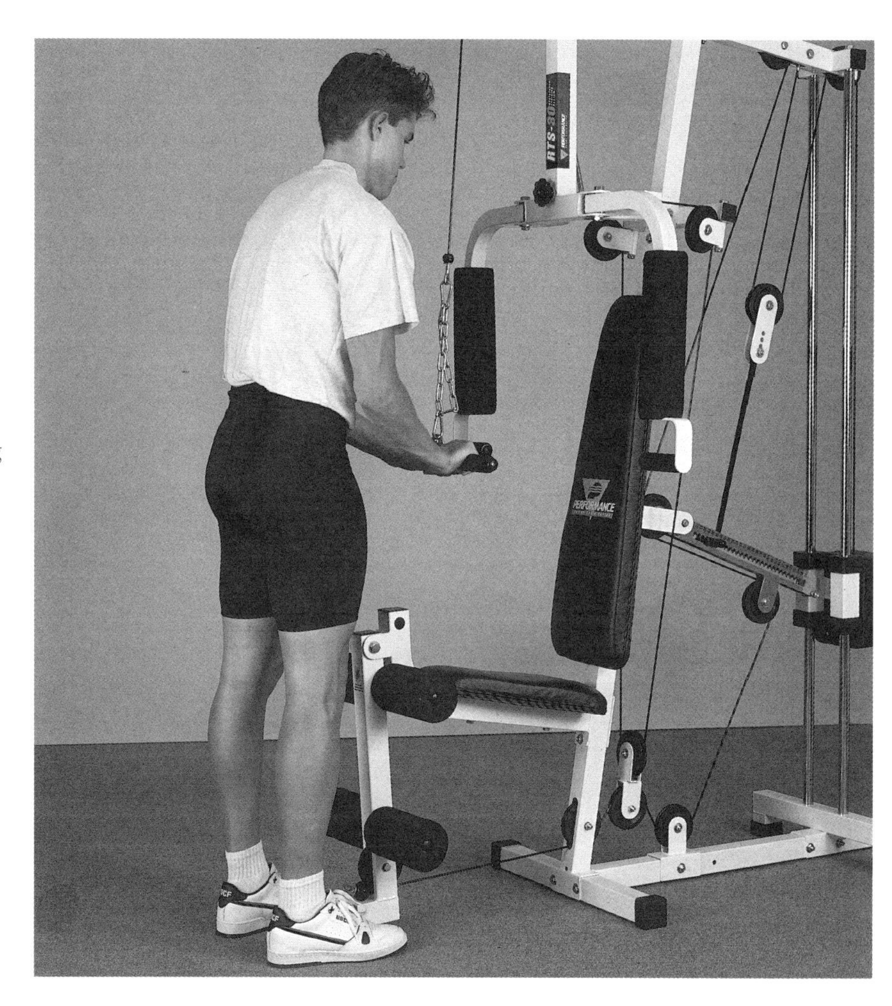

Upper Body Pulling Exercises

Upper body pulling exercises involve some form of elbow flexion (bending of the elbow joint). The upper body is particularly important in its contribution to added strength and power in climbing hills or in sprinting.

Recommended RTS-30 upper body pulling exercises include:

- Lat Machine Pull Down
- Bent-Over Rowing
- Arm Curl
- Upright Rowing

Arm Curl

- Preparation: Fit foot brace in mid position. Fit t-bar and chain to low pulley. Adjust length so arms can fully extend in the lowered position. Stand on foot brace.

- Description: Grip the bar with palms up. Keep arms straight and elbows in contact with torso. Slowly bend the elbows and wrists to "curl" the bar to a position touching the neck.

- Cycling Application: Sprinting, hill climbing and any pulling motion on the handlebars.

- Muscles: Biceps and other forearm flexors.

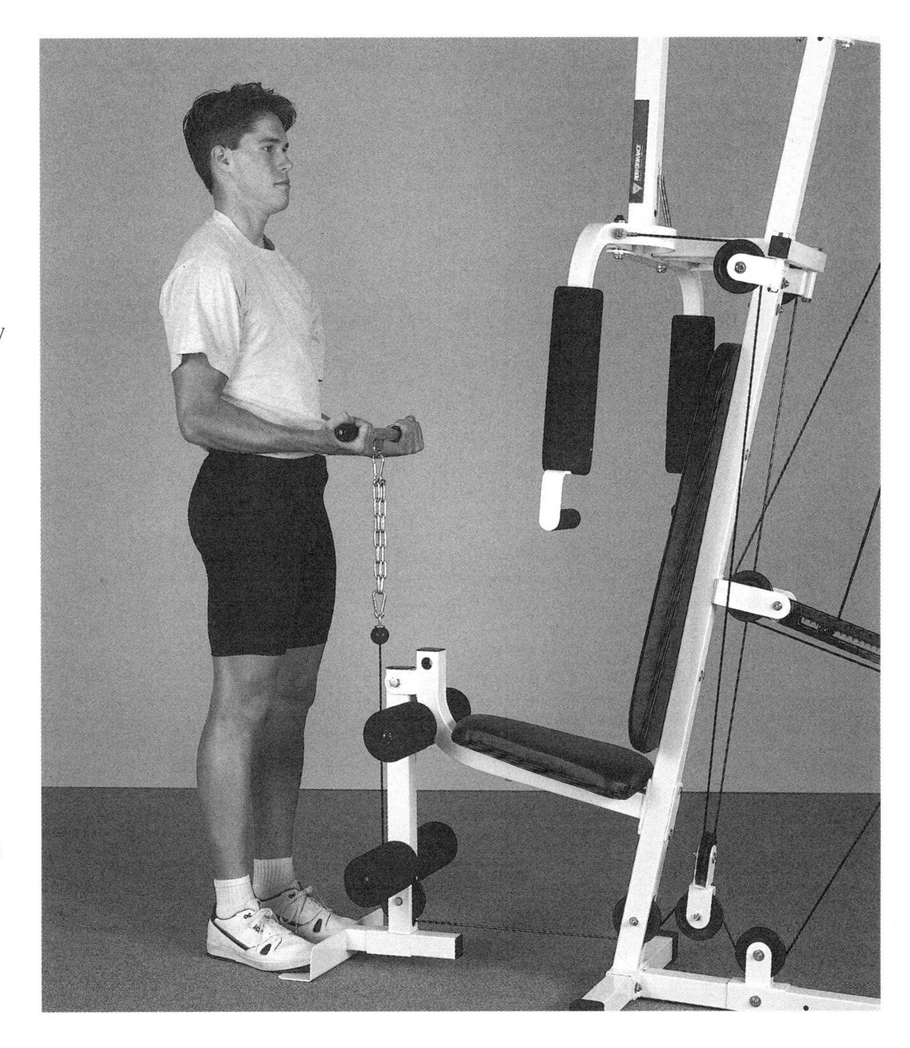

Lat Machine Pull Down

- Preparation: Fit lat bar to high pulley and roll pads to top hole. Sit on bench with thighs secured by upper roll pads. Torso should be 4"- 6" in front of back pad.

- Description: Grip handles with an overhand grip, using narrow, medium or wide grip. Be sure arms stretch fully over head. Pull the bar down until bar touches upper back. Slowly return to starting position.

- Cycling Application: Upper body support while on handlebars, overall balance of body muscularity/strength and pulling on bars while climbing.

- Muscles: Biceps, rhomboids and pectorals.

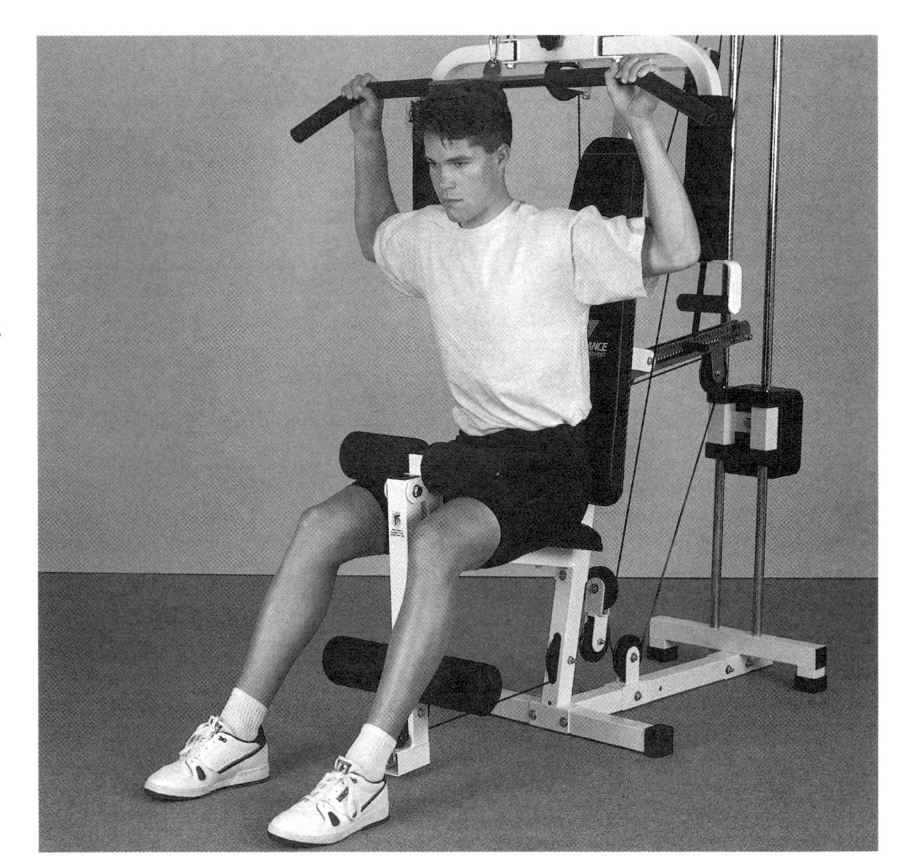

Bent Over Rowing

- Preparation: Fit foot brace and slide it out as far as possible. Fit bar with chain to low pulley and adjust length.

- Description: Keep back flat, with shoulders slightly higher than hips. Keep knees slightly bent throughout the lift. Grip may vary due to shoulder width. From a fully extended arm position, bend the elbows and pull bar until it touches the lower chest or upper abdomen. Slowly return to starting position.

- Cycling Application: Pulling on the bars during sprints or climbing.

- Muscles: Latissimus dorsi, biceps brachii and posterior deltoid.

Upright Row

- Preparation: Fit foot brace and t-bar to low pulley with chain. Adjust length so that arms can fully extend in the lowered position.

- Description: Stand on foot brace and grip the bar with index fingers about 4" apart and palms facing body. Pull upwards by bending elbows. Keep the bar as close to the body as possible and pull until the bar is under the chin. Elbows should be higher than the bar throughout the entire movement. Slowly return to the starting position.

- Cycling Application: Sprinting, hill climbing and any pulling motion on the handlebars.

- Muscles: Biceps, deltoids and trapezius.

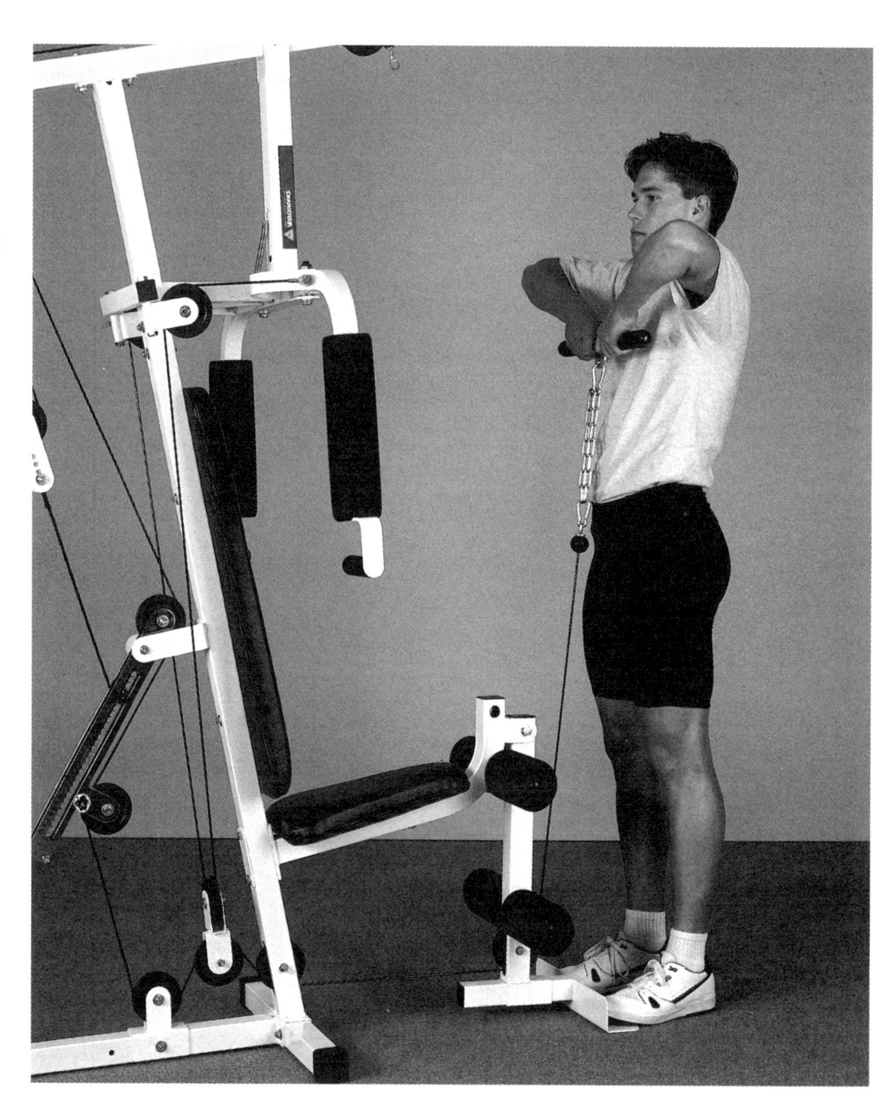

Lower Back Exercises

Lower back exercises are important since this part of the body is where many cyclists feel fatigue, especially early in the season or on long rides. While cyclists tend to be quite flexible in the area of trunk flexion (bending forward), they are typically poor at trunk extension (bending in the other direction). Training the lower back muscles will help improve posture and will most likely help transfer more force to the pedals, especially in seated, climbing situations.

Recommended RTS-30 lower back exercises include:

- Back Extension
- Low Cable Pull (can be considered upper body pulling)
- Stiff Leg Dead Lift

Back Extension

- Preparation: If needed pad seat area with towels for added comfort and to level the seat. Place hips on padded area and hold your legs straight behind with a training partner securely holding ankles.
- Description: With hands behind the head, slowly lower torso as low as possible (head touches floor) and return to the starting position (torso parallel to the floor). Do not rise above this position.
- Cycling Application: Torso position, climbing while seated, posture, stability while sprinting and pedal stroke.

- Muscles: Spinal erectors (spinalis dorsi, longissimus dorsi and ilio costalis lumborum).

Low Pulley Row

- Preparation: Fit foot brace and slide it completely in. Fit t-bar to low pulley.

- Description: Sit with feet against foot brace and legs slightly bent. Grip the bar with an overhand grip with hands about shoulder width apart. Starting position is with torso leaning forward slightly. Begin by moving the torso to a position perpendicular to the floor, with the arms still straight. Finish the movement by bending the elbows and pulling the bar to the abdomen.

- Cycling Application: Sprinting and hill climbing.

- Muscles: Latissimus dorsi, biceps brachii and spinal erectors.

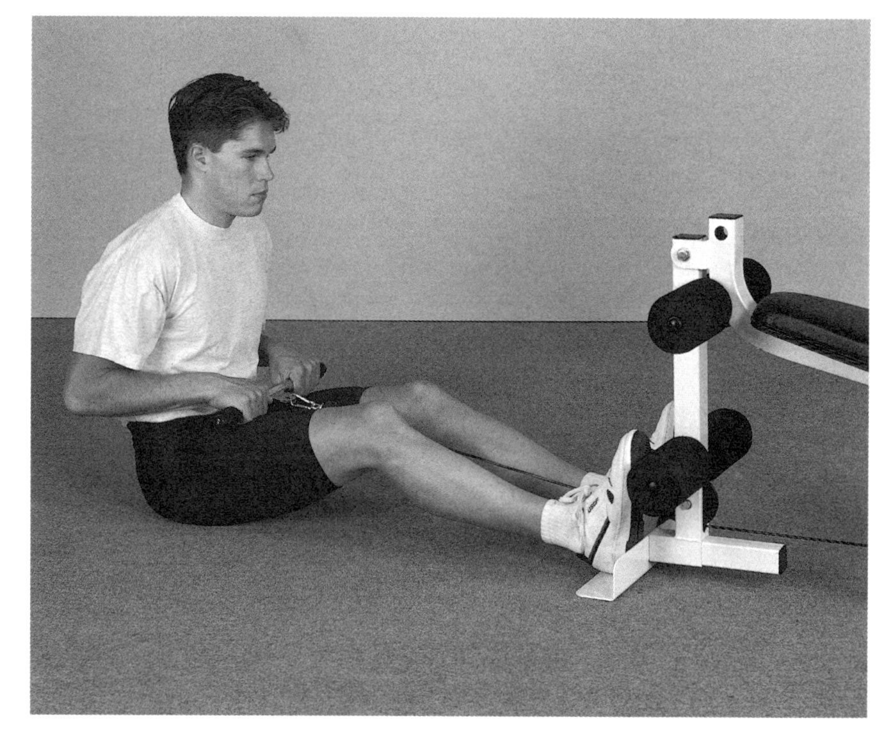

Stiff Leg Dead Lift

- Preparation: Fit foot brace in and t-bar to low pulley with chain.

- Description: Keeping knees slightly bent, bend the torso at the hips and waist. Grasp the bar with an over hand grip. Slowly straighten the torso until the body is fully erect. This exercise can be performed with the lower back flat or rounded. The flat back is considered safer, but more difficult to perform.

- Cycling Application: Torso position, climbing while seated, posture, stability while sprinting and pedal stroke.

- Muscles: Spinal erectors, hamstrings and gluteals.

Abdominal Exercises

One of the weakest areas for cyclists (and most others) is the abdominal muscles. This affects the pedaling power in sprints, climbing and time trials, as well as contributing to lower back pain. Just looking at the posture of the average cyclist on aero or conventional bars suggests that the abdominal muscles are usually not in an active state. A bit of strength training here can really pay off, particularly in climbing or sprinting out of the saddle.

Recommended RTS-30 abdominal exercises include the following:

- Pulley Crunch
- Side Bends

Pulley Crunch

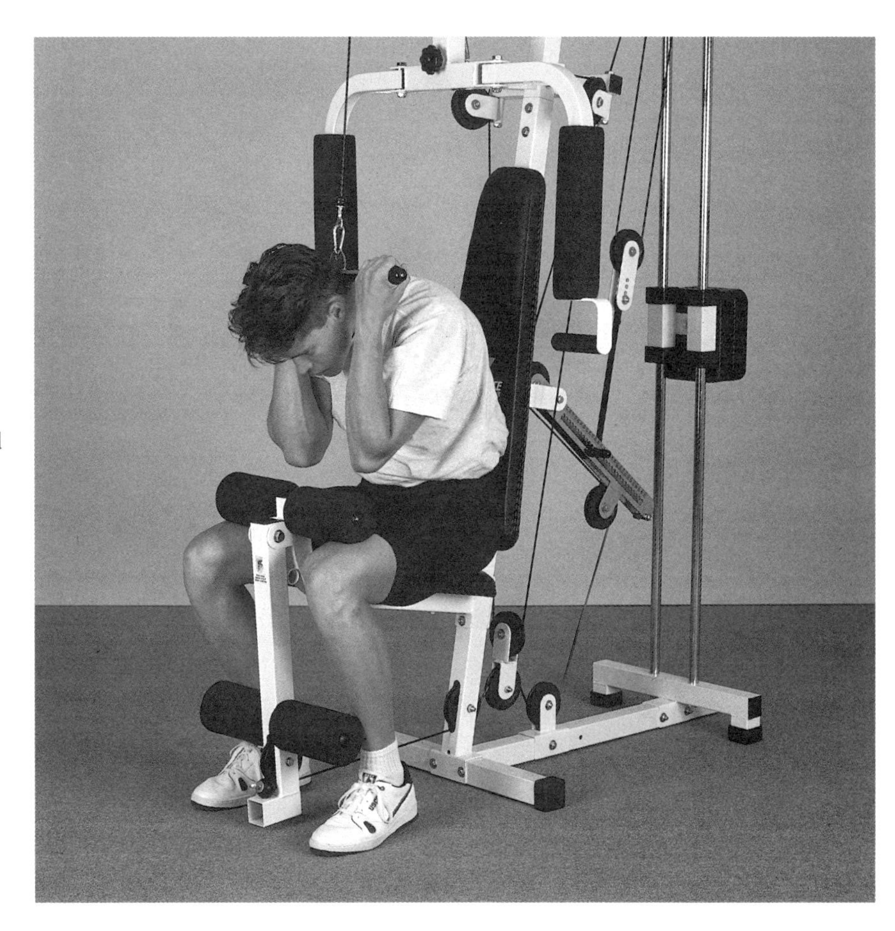

- Preparation: Fit t-bar to high pulley and roll pads to bottom hole.
- Description: Hook legs around the roll pads and grip the bar at the back of the head. Bend at the waist and curl down and forward until elbows contact upper roller pad.
- Cycling Application: Trunk stabilization (especially on drops) and climbing.
- Muscles: Rectus abdominals.

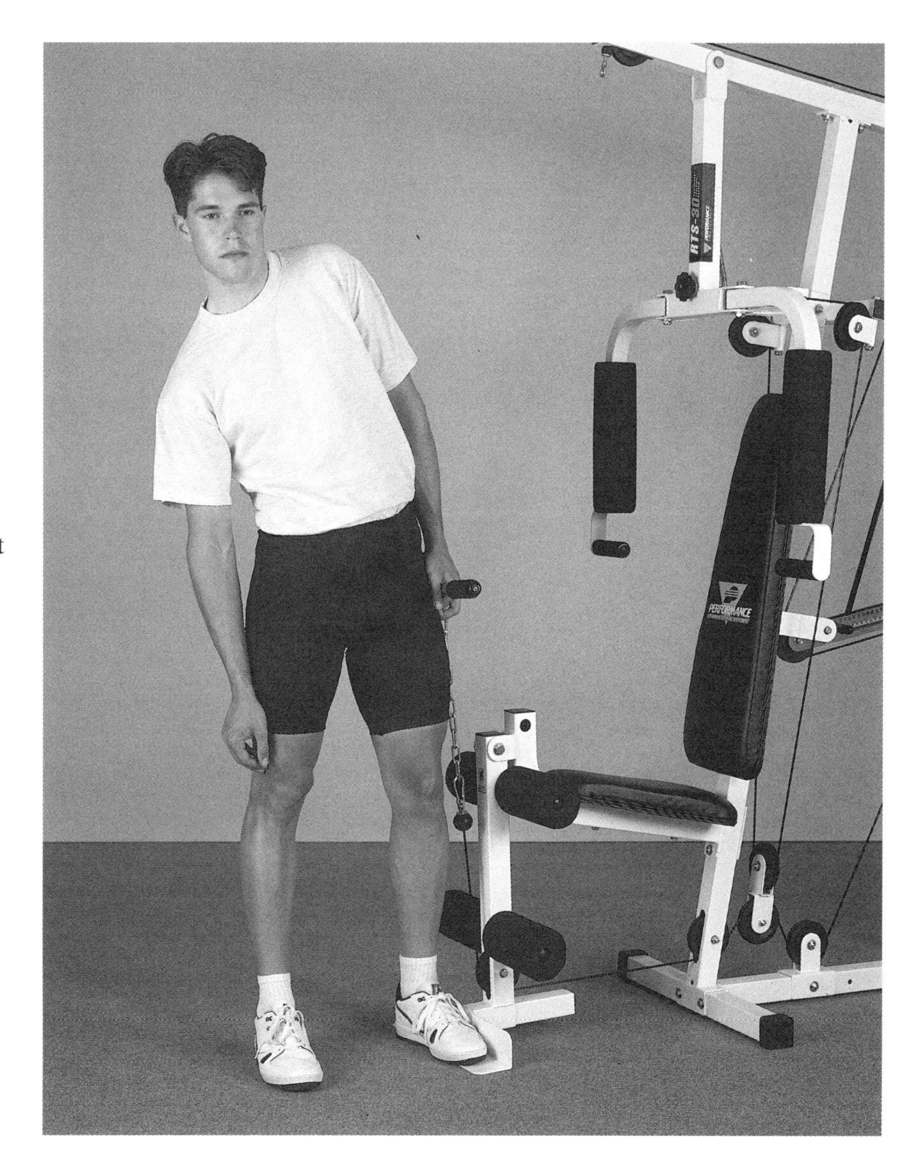

Side Bends

- Preparation: Fit foot brace and t-bar to low pulley. Use chain to adjust length.

- Description: Stand 90 degrees from RTS-30, with foot closest to unit on foot brace. Allow weight to pull hand grasping bar down to approximately knee position. Flex the opposite oblique abdominal muscle to return torso to upright position. Change to opposite side and repeat.

- Cycling Application: Out-of-saddle climbing/sprints.

- Muscles: Abdominal obliques.

Lower Body Exercises

Most cyclists tend to prioritize the lower body when they strength train. In some instances, this is an error, since more strength may be needed in the upper body in order to obtain faster speed on your bike. Cyclists' legs tend to be above average in strength as a result of riding. The pedal stroke is mostly dependent on hip flexion and hip extension, along with knee flexion and extension. The calf, or lower leg, is not thought to contribute greatly to the pedal stroke, but some work should be directed here.

Recommended RTS-30 lower body exercises include the following:

- Hack Squats
- Jefferson or Straddle Lift
- Leg Extensions
- Leg Curls
- Heel or Calf Raises
- Hip Flexion
- Hip Extension

Hip Flexion

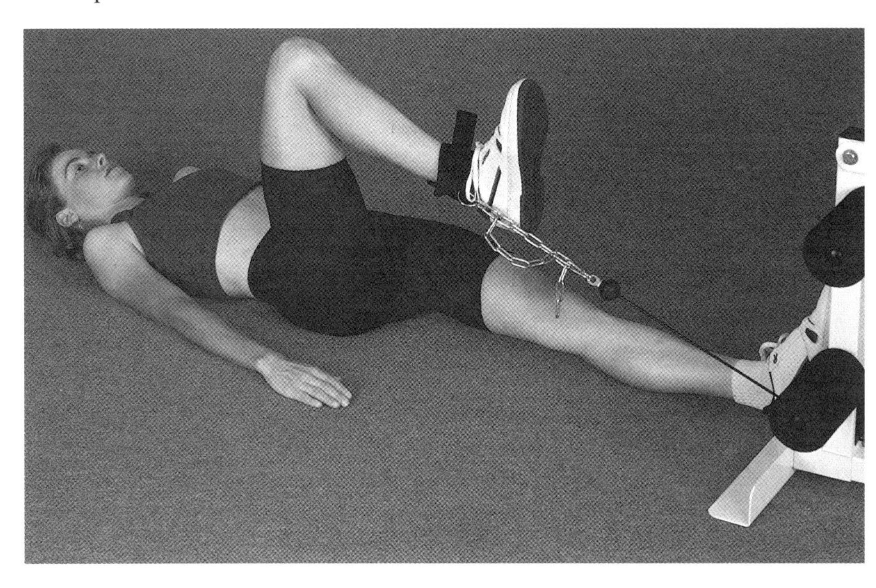

- Preparation: Fit foot brace and slide it completely in. Fit ankle cuff to low pulley, then fit cuff around right ankle. Lie on back (supine), with legs straight. Keep left foot in contact with foot brace.

- Description: Bend hip and knee to bring knee as close as possible to chest. Switch ankles and repeat.

- Cycling Application: Pedal stroke.

- Muscles: Hip flexors (psoas minor, psoas major and illacus).

Hip Extension

- Preparation: Fit ankle cuff to low pulley. Place cuff around right ankle.
- Description: Face RTS and hold on for balance. Keeping knee straight, raise foot as high as possible behind body in a kicking motion. Slowly return to starting position. Switch ankles and repeat.
- Cycling Application: Pedal stroke.
- Muscles: Gluteus maximus and hamstrings.

Hack Squats

- Preparation: Fit foot brace and slide it out as far as possible. Fit T-bar with chain to low pulley and adjust length. Place a small board on top of the foot brace.

- Description: Place heels on board and bend knees until thighs are approximately parallel to the floor. Grasp bar with overhand grip behind hips with arms straight. Maintain a flat back. Straighten knees, slowly re-bend to starting position.

- Cycling Application: Pedal stroke.

- Muscles: Quadriceps, gluteals, hip extensors, spinal erectors and calf muscles (gastrocnemius and soleus).

Jefferson or Straddle Lift

- Preparation: Fit foot brace and slide it out as far as possible. Fit T-bar with chain to low pulley and adjust length.

- Description: Stand facing RTS-30, with left foot on foot brace and right foot approximately 18 - 24 inches behind. Bend knees while keeping front foot flat and grasp bar between legs. Straighten knees, slowly return to starting position. Switch to right foot and repeat.

- Cycling Application: Pedal stroke.

- Muscles: Quadriceps, gluteals and hip extensors (gluteus maximus and hamstrings).

Leg Extension

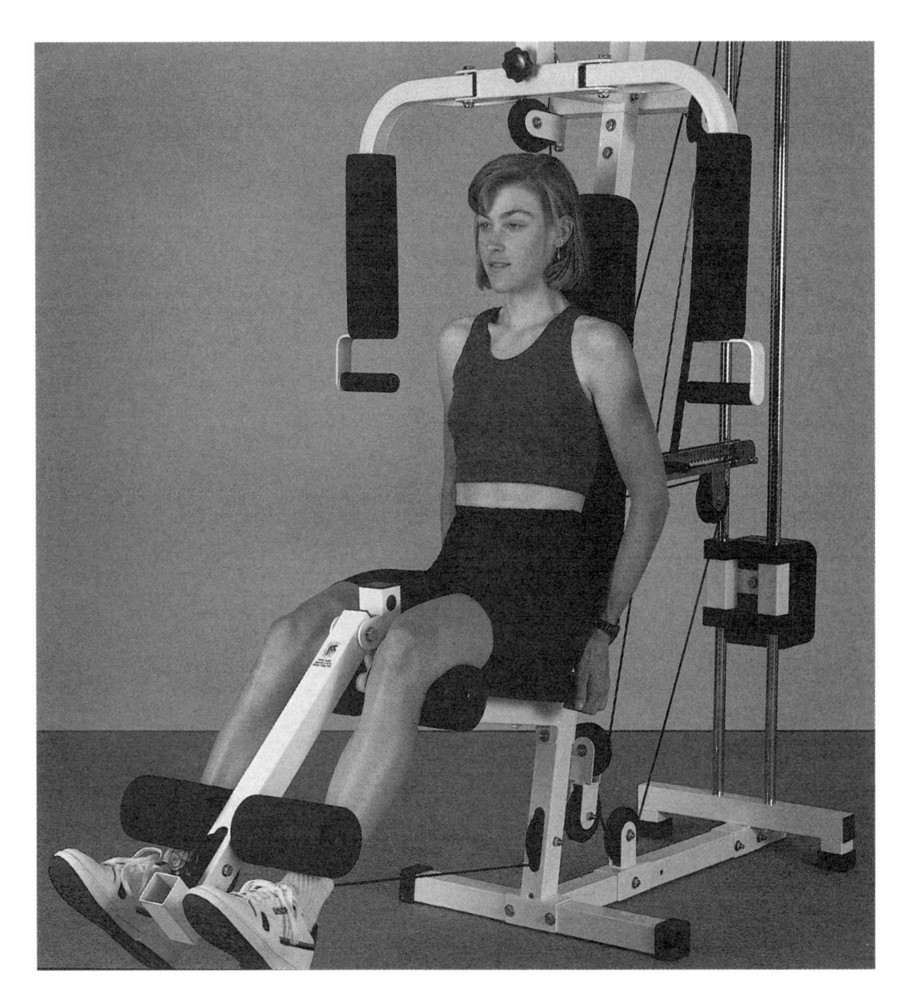

- Preparation: Fit roll pads to bottom hole position. From a standing position place feet behind lower set of roll pads and sit down. Grip the bottom of the seat.

- Description: Keeping torso flat against back pad, slowly straighten knees and return to starting position.

- Cycling Application: Prepares quadriceps for multi-joint exercises which aids in your pedal stroke.

- Muscles: Quadriceps.

Leg Curl

- Preparation: Fit the roll pads to the top hole. Facing the RTS-30, hook leg around the lower roll pad. Grasp the top of the seat back padding for balance.

- Description: Slowly bend knee to raise lower leg as high as possible. Return to starting position. Repeat exercise using opposite leg.

- Cycling Application: Pedal stroke.

- Muscles: Hamstrings.

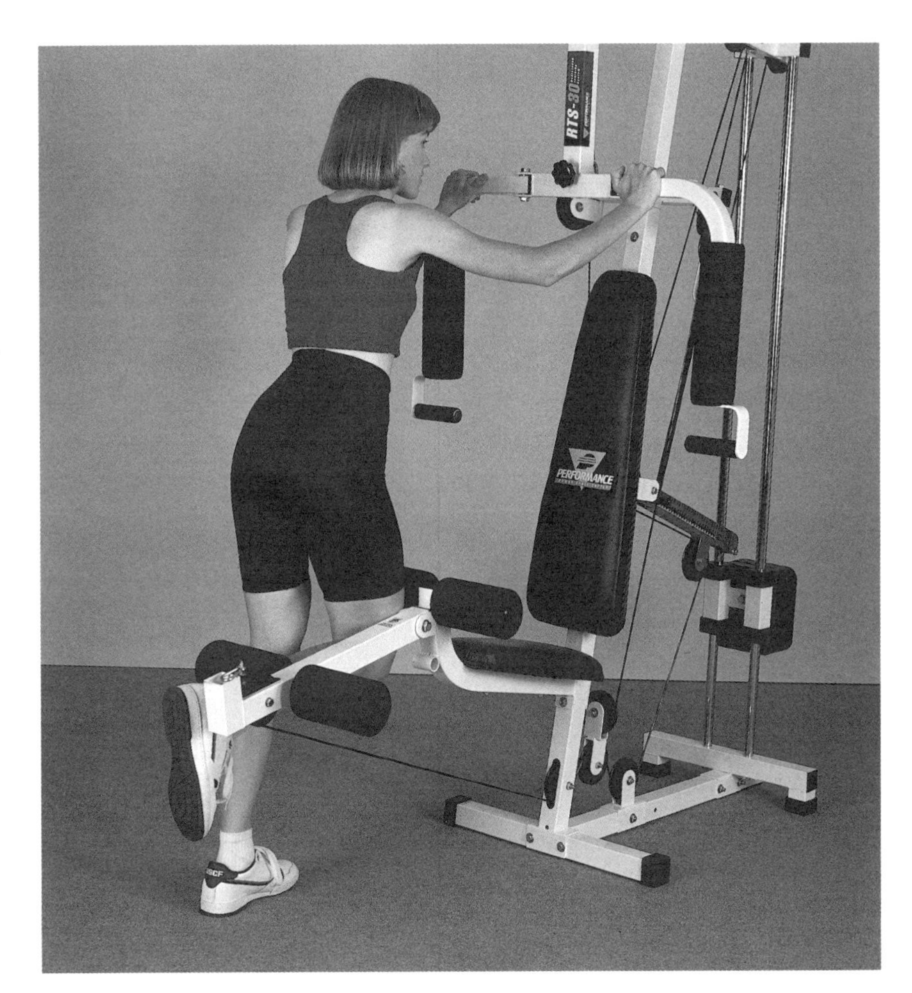

Heel or Calf Raises

- Preparation: Fit foot brace and slide it out as far as possible. Fit T-bar with chain to low pulley and adjust length. Place small board on top of foot brace.

- Description: Facing RTS-30, grasp bar with overhand grip and place toes on top of board. Keeping legs straight, slowly rise up on toes. Slowly lower heel to floor.

- Cycling Application: Pedal stroke.

- Muscles: Gastrocnemius and soleus.

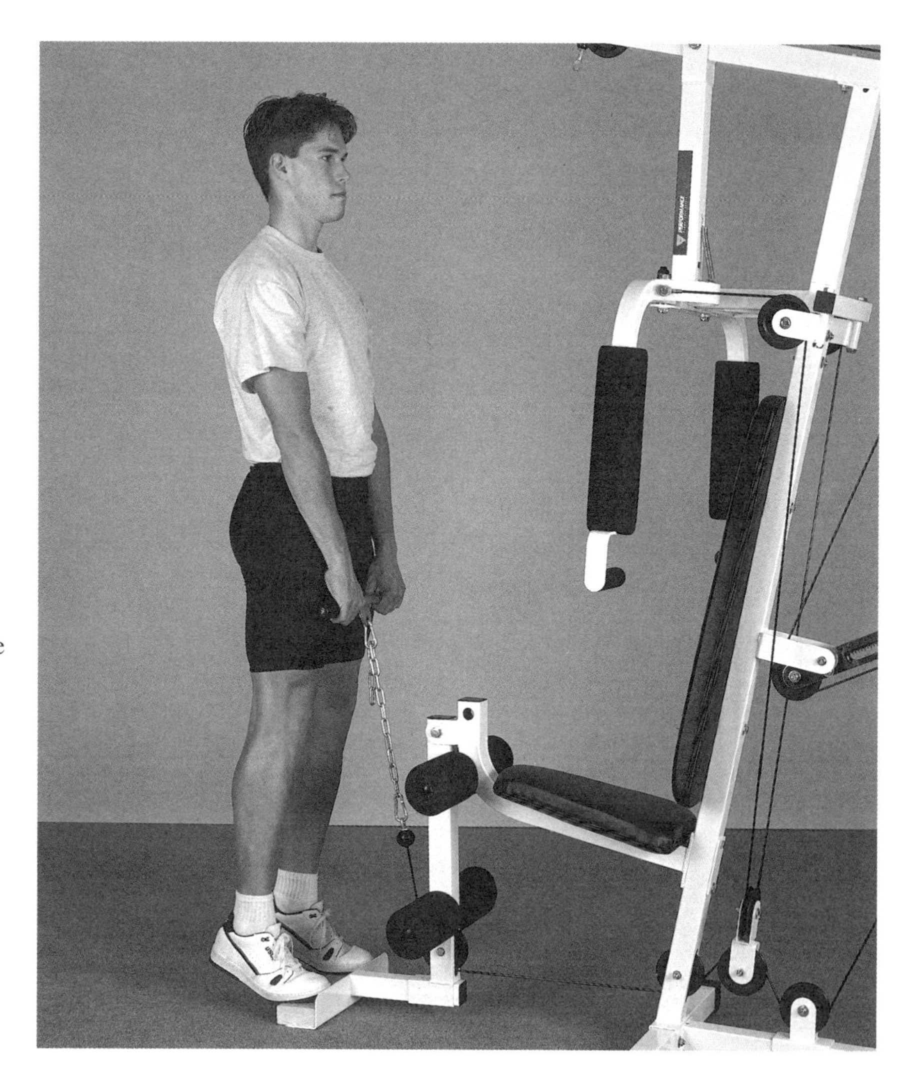

Supplemental or Specialty Exercises

Certain supplemental exercises are also available, although they do not fit directly into any of the above five categories. These exercises may be used to add variety to the workout, or to address specific individual weaknesses.

RTS-30 supplemental exercises include the following:

- Flys
- Wrist Curls
- Reverse Wrist Curls
- Shrugs
- Reverse Curls
- Hip Adduction
- Hip Abduction

Flys

- Preparation: Engage lock lever and move roll pads to top hole for leg room if required.

- Description: From the seated position place elbows or upper arms against the bottom of the roll pads. Bring your elbows together so pads touch in front. Return slowly to the starting position. Maintain only a light grip with the hands, allowing the chest muscles to perform the work.

- Cycling Application: Upper body support while on handlebars and overall balance of body muscularity/ strength.

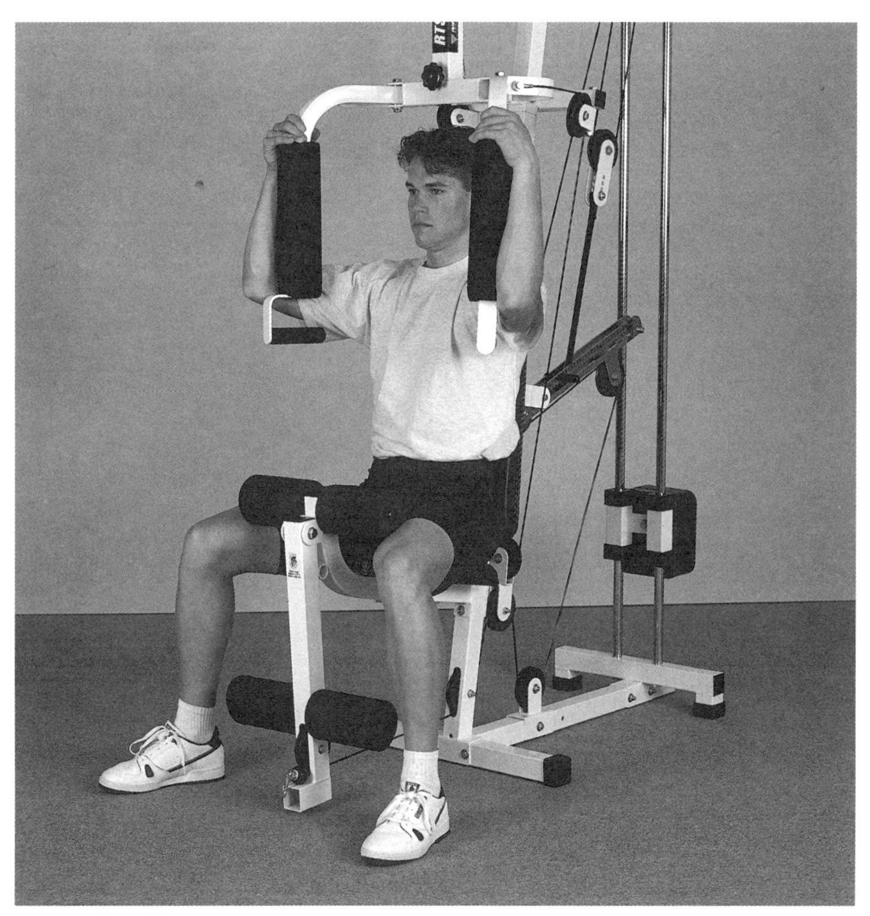

- Muscles: Chest or pectorals.

Wrist Curls

- Preparation: Fit t-bar to low pulley and roll pads to top hole.

- Description: Sit on seat and rest forearms on roll pads. Grip the bar with palms up. Keeping elbows stationary, flex wrists until palms are above parallel to the ground. Slowly return to starting position.

- Cycling Application: Aids in overall gripping strength, which is particularly important for mountain bike riding.

- Muscles: Forearm flexors.

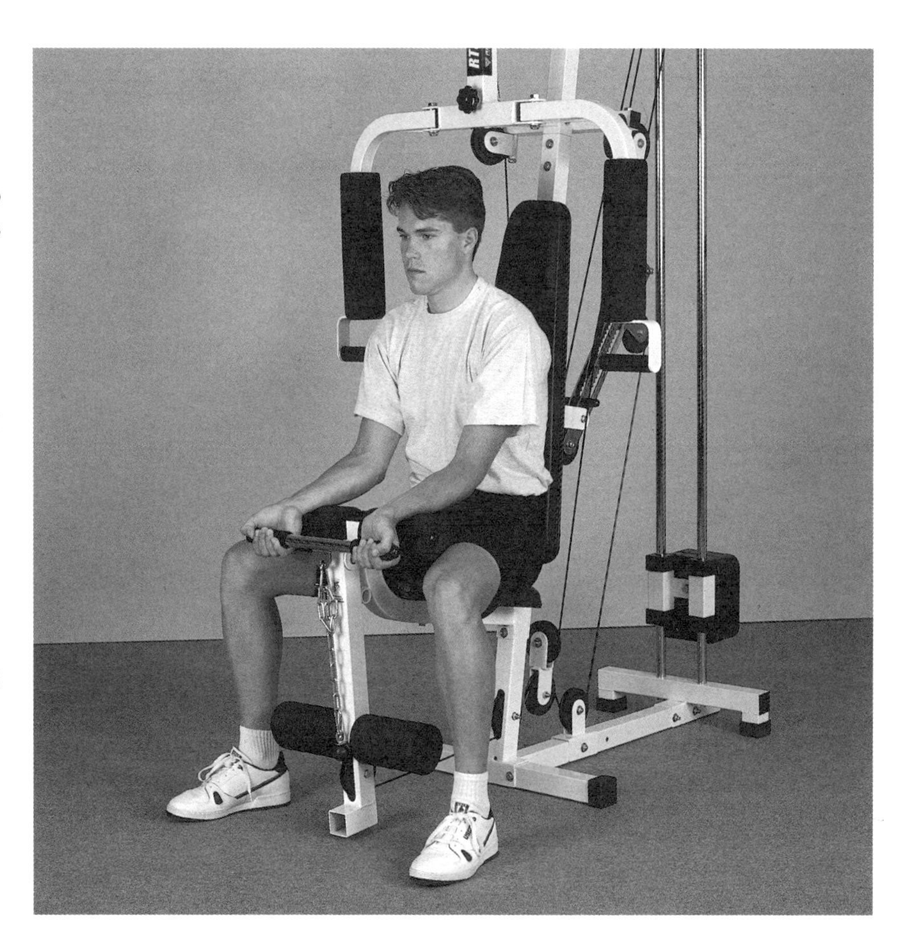

Reverse Wrist Curl

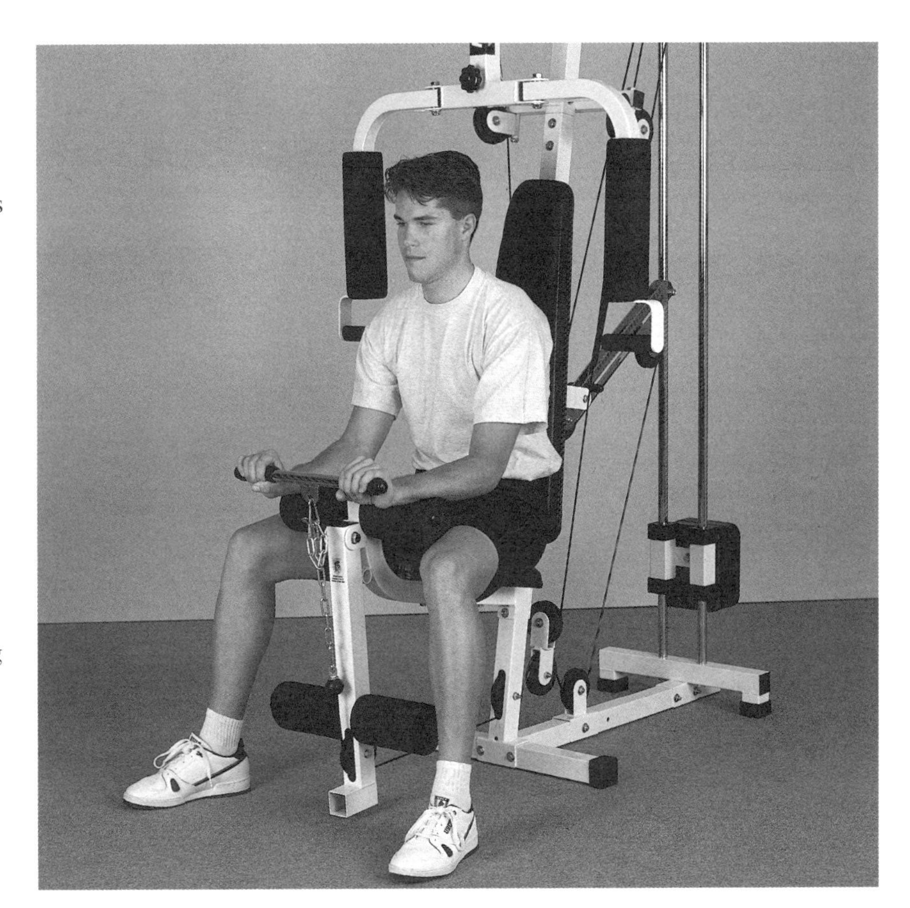

- Preparation: Fit t-bar to low pulley and roll pads to top hole.
- Description: Sit on seat and rest forearms on roll pads. Grip bar with palms down. Keeping elbows stationary, flex wrists until palms are above parallel to the ground. Slowly return to starting position.
- Cycling Application: Aids in overall gripping strength, which is particularly important for mountain bike riding.
- Muscles: Forearm extensors.

Shrugs

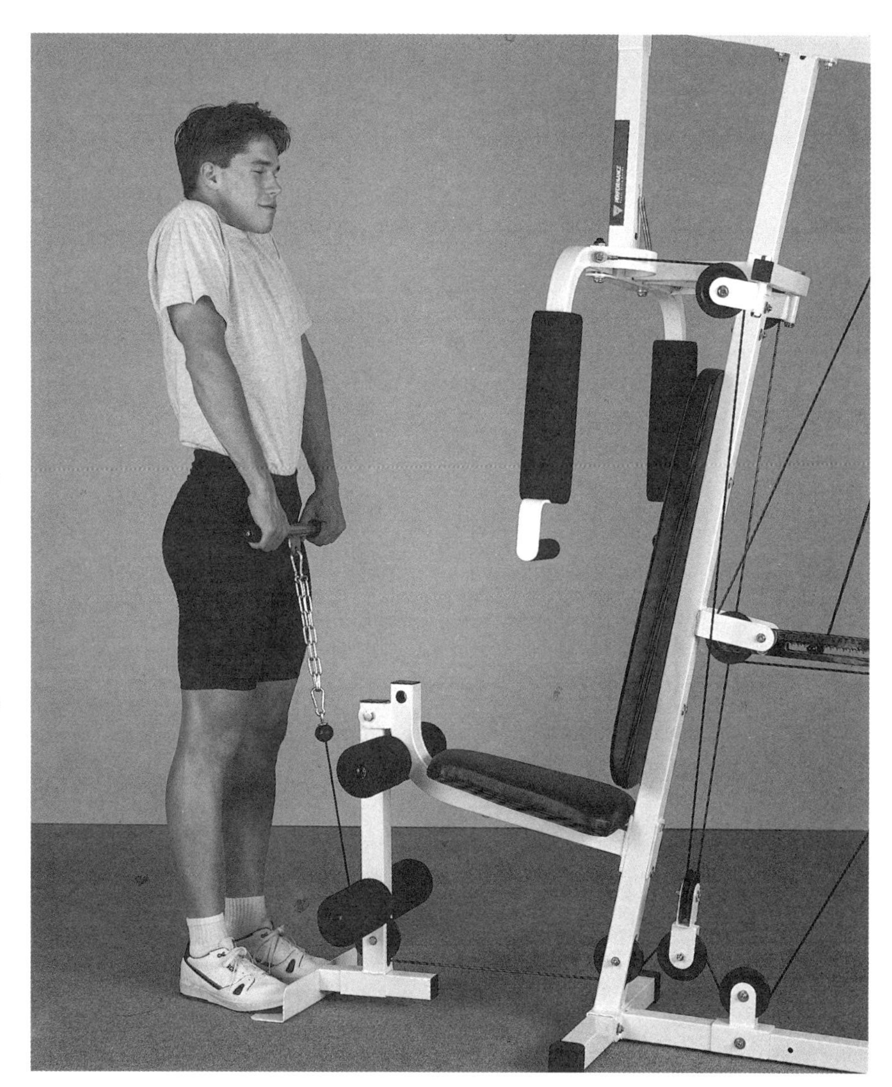

- Preparation: Fit foot brace and fit T-bar with chain to low pulley. Adjust the length.
- Description: Stand on foot brace and grasp the T-bar with palms down and your grip about shoulder width apart. Contract the trapezius muscles of the upper back in a shrugging motion. Slowly lower to starting position. Shoulders should travel straight up and down.
- Cycling Application: Reduces fatigue in the neck area, especially on long rides. Helps with out-of-saddle climbing.
- Muscles: Trapezius.

Reverse Curl

- Preparation: Fit foot brace in the mid position and fit t-bar and chain to lower pulley. Adjust the length

- Description: Stand on foot brace and grip the t-bar with an overhand grip. Keep elbows touching the side of your torso. Bend elbows until the bar is raised to neck level while elbows rotate under the bar. Slowly return to starting position.

- Cycling Application: Pulling on handlebars during sprinting, hill climbing, etc.

- Muscles: Biceps, biceps brachii and forearm extensors.

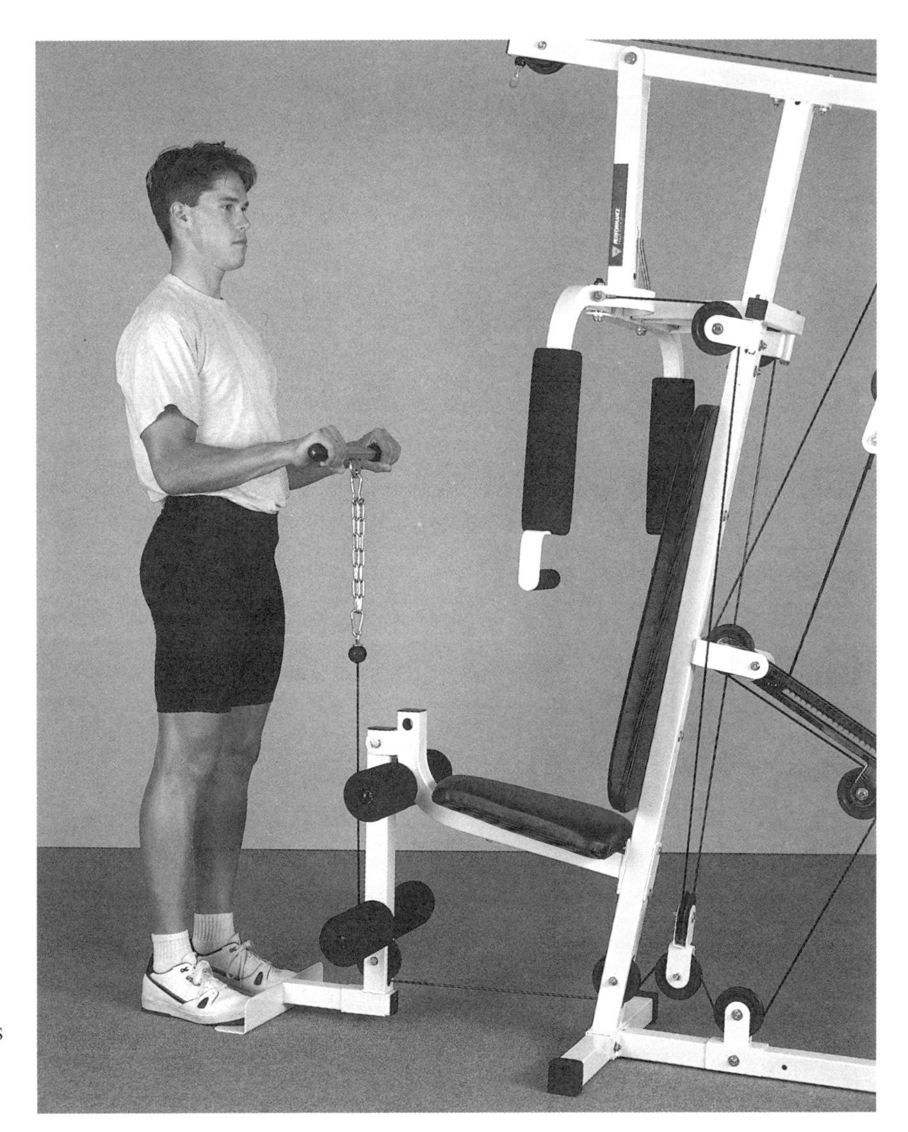

Hip Adduction

- Preparation: Fit ankle cuff to low pulley then fit the cuff around left ankle.
- Description: Face 90 degrees to the right from the RTS-30. To keep your balance hold the top of the bench. Keeping your left knee straight, bring your left foot across your right leg and raise it as high as possible. Lower to starting position. Switch the cuff to the right ankle and repeat.
- Cycling Application: Maintains supporting hip musculature and contributes to stable and strong pedal stroke.
- Muscles: Tensor fasciae latae, gracilis and pectineus.

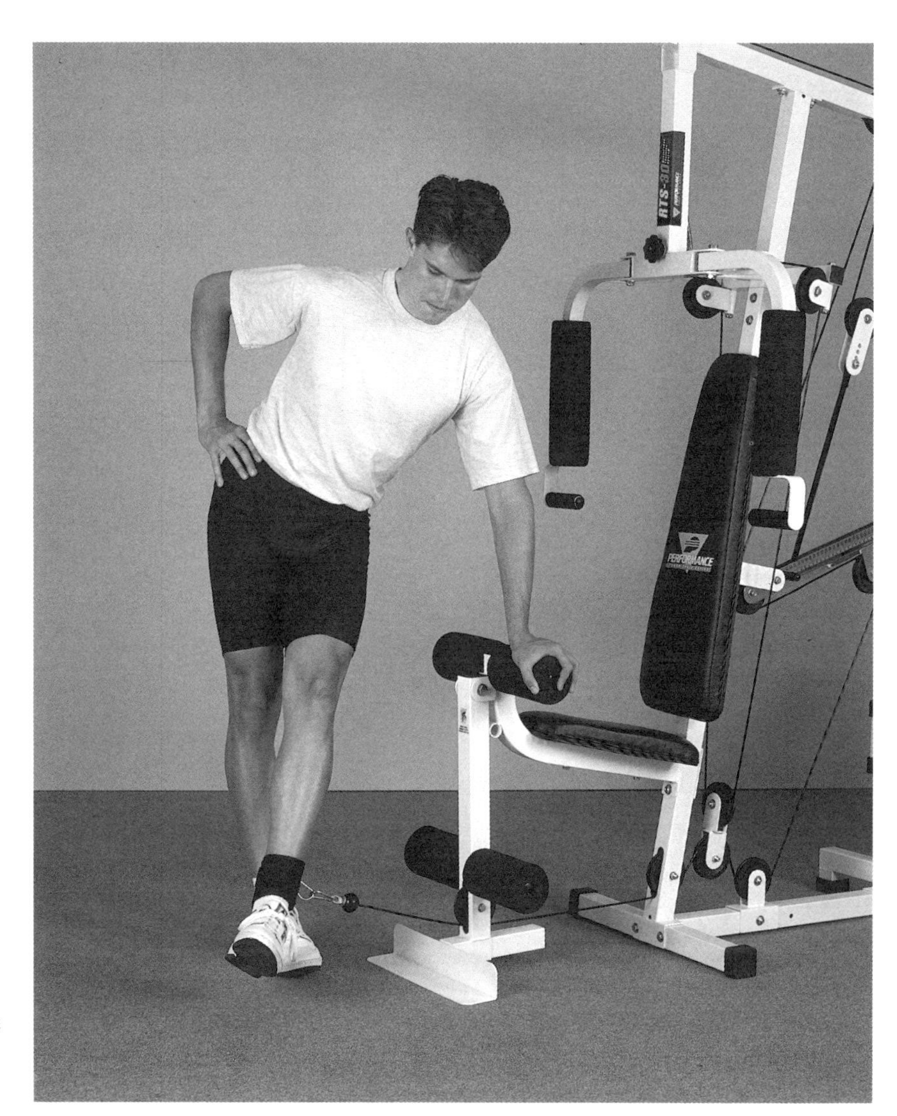

Hip Abduction Together

- Preparation: Set up as for hip adduction, but place the ankle cuff on your right ankle.
- Description: Keeping your right knee straight, raise your right foot out to the side as far as possible. Slowly return to the starting position. Switch the cuff to the left ankle and repeat.
- Cycling Application: Maintains supporting hip musculature and contributes to stable and strong pedal stroke.
- Muscles: Tensor fasciae latae, sartorius, gluteus medius and minimus.

Workouts

Now that you are familiar with the types of exercises that will benefit your cycling performance, the following series is suggested for implementing a strength training program. First, pick at least one exercise from each of the first five groups. Add one or two exercises from the last category which you think would benefit you the most. Second, depending on which phase you are training in, determine the appropriate number of sets and reps you will perform. Last, and most important, determine how much weight you can lift during each set. Your first set is a warm-up and should be 50% of what you can perform on your last set.

Progressive Resistance

Understanding the principle of Progressive Resistance is a must in order to gain progress in your strength training schedule. This means that you must regularly strive to improve your best record in a particular movement for an assigned number of reps. Once you can consistently perform more than one set for the assigned number of reps, you should increase the load in your next workout.

Most likely, you will decrease the number of reps you can perform until your body adapts to the new load, but this is how strength gains are made. Just as you would not expect to make improvements on your bike by always riding over the same course, in the same gear and at the same speed, the principle behind Progressive Resistance is that you should not settle into the same workout pattern. What follows is a chart showing an example of progressive resistance training for one exercise.

Category - Upper Body Pushing *Exercise - Chest Press*				
Date: Week of 10/3 *Weight/reps*	*Set 1* *40/15*	*Set 2* *60/12*	*Set 3* *80/10*	*notes:* *increase reps*
Date: Week of 10/10 *Weight/reps*	*Set 1* *40/15*	*Set 2* *60/14*	*Set 3* *80/13*	*notes:* *increase reps*
Date: Week of 10/17 *Weight/reps*	*Set 1* *40/15*	*Set 2* *60/15*	*Set 3* *80/15*	*notes:* *increase weight*
Date: Week of 10/24 *Weight/reps*	*Set 1* *45/12*	*Set 2* *70/12*	*Set 3* *90/10*	*notes:* *increase reps*
Date: Week of 11/1 *Weight/reps*	*Set 1* *45/13*	*Set 2* *70/13*	*Set 3* *90/11*	*notes:* *increase reps*
Date: Week of 11/8 *Weight/reps*	*Set 1* *45/15*	*Set 2* *70/15*	*Set 3* *90/12*	*notes:* *increase weight*

Workout Tips

Besides Progressive Resistance there are other "tricks of the trade" to keep you challenged in your strength training program. For example, change exercises around about every four weeks. Even though you will have a favorite exercise in each category, it is essential to incorporate all of them into your training program. Also, switch the order of your strength training exercises. For example, if you always start your training with the Chest Press exercise, move it occasionally to the middle or end of your exercise regimen.

Regardless of the training phase, your first set or two should be viewed as a warm-up, without maximum effort. Be sure you add resistance after each set so the last set(s) will be difficult. If you are using lower reps (as in a Strength Phase), be sure the first set or two is with higher reps (8-12) in order to have a proper warm-up.

It is also a good idea to reduce training intensity every four to six weeks, still performing the exercises, but with less weight. This "unloading" allows the body to recover and usually will result in improvement within a few weeks. Be sure to start back with a moderate weight with which you can use proper technique.

Injury Prevention

- Do not hold your breath during exertion. Slowly exhale during exertion and inhale during the recovery phase. Holding your breath may result in a valsalva maneuver, in which blood flow is temporarily cut off resulting in higher blood pressure and the possibility of blacking out.
- Always warm-up prior to resistance training. Jogging in place, jumping jacks, skipping rope or cycling on a stationary bike for a few minutes are excellent warm-ups. This will increase the muscles' temperature and also raise respiration and heart rate.
- Always cool-down after a workout. Spend some time on a bike (stationary or otherwise) or take a brisk walk. Also include some stretching.
- Work through a full range of motion. This means opening the affected joints completely and closing them completely. Performing an exercise through a limited range of motion may lead to injury or a lack of flexibility.
- The use of a weight lifting belt is optional. A belt is generally overrated and does not reduce the likelihood of injury. If a belt is used, keep it snug during lifting and loosen it between sets.
- The use of gloves may help reduce skin damage, such as callouses to the hands. Regular cycling gloves work very well.
- Always perform your first set with a resistance you can easily complete, usually about 50-60% of your maximum assigned number of reps for your last set(s).
- Dress warmly to help prevent injuries, especially during the cold months.

Weight Training Safety Tips

- Check your equipment (machine cables, pulleys, pins) for wear and tear.
- Never place your hands on the pulley system or reach under the lifted plate supplying resistance. Check the lever that locks the bench arm and brings the butterfly into action when in use.
- Don't attempt to lift too much weight.
- Don't drop the weight block at the end of a repetition; lower it gently to the rubber bumper.
- Place your hands or feet on the machine with care, so they will not slip off the roll pads or bars.
- If possible, strength train with another person for spotting purposes, especially if you use free weights.

Summary

You now have the know-how to begin your strength training program. Be sure to select a weight you can comfortably lift for the prescribed number of repetitions. Be sure to perform the first set of each exercise with a resistance approximately 50-60% of what you expect to lift on your last set. Add weight on the succeeding sets. Keep accurate records of the amount of weight you lift. Make periodic attempts at improving the amount of weight you use on your last set or two. Your health is the number one priority, so be careful with your lifting technique and the equipment you use. Strength training can improve your cycling performance, but you still need to convert this strength to on-bike performance.

Chapter 4 Aerobic Training

What exactly is aerobic fitness? Being fit for most individuals means having more energy to perform daily tasks, being more active, and not tiring easily. Fitness to a competitive cyclist means riding comfortably for several hours at 20 mph or faster.

Regular exercise brings gains in many ways:

- It improves blood circulation throughout the body. Lungs, heart and muscles work together more efficiently.
- Along with proper diet, it can help control body weight.
- It relieves tension and helps you relax and sleep better.
- It increases stamina.
- It helps the body make the best use of fats and sugars.
- It reduces elevated blood pressure that can lead to an increased risk of cardiovascular disease.

Heart Rate

It is easy to monitor progress in your strength training program since you always will be increasing the number of reps or the amount of weight you are lifting. If you keep a training log it is simple to glance through and see your improvements. Aerobic training, however, is not as clear cut. Your 20 to 60 minute aerobic workout may feel easier, but you can actually quantify your improvements only by monitoring your heart rate.

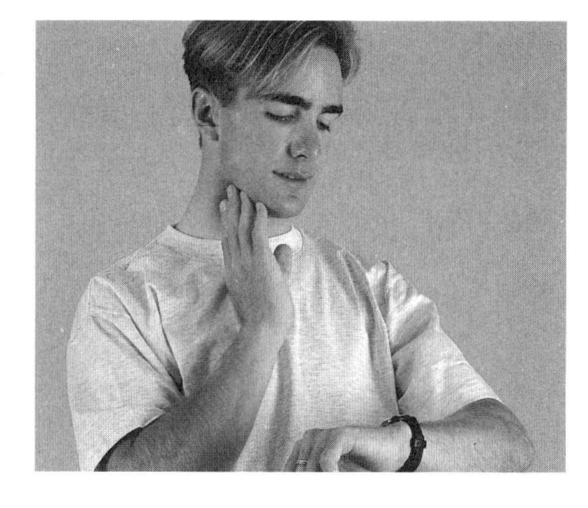

Monitoring your heart rate is the easiest way of determining how hard you are exercising. Your pulse can easily be felt at your wrist or at the carotid artery, located on the side of your neck. Practice taking your pulse for 10 seconds while at rest and while exercising. Take this 10 second count and multiply it by 6 to come out with beats per minute (bpm).

While counting your pulse may seem straightforward, it may not be the most accurate or convenient method of measuring your heart rate. If you find it difficult to count while exercising, then use the ear-clip photo reflectance unit that comes with specific pieces of Performance exercise equipment, or consider purchasing an electronic wireless heart rate monitor.

Thanks to modern electronics, portable wireless heart rate monitors are available that can measure heart rate with the accuracy of expensive laboratory

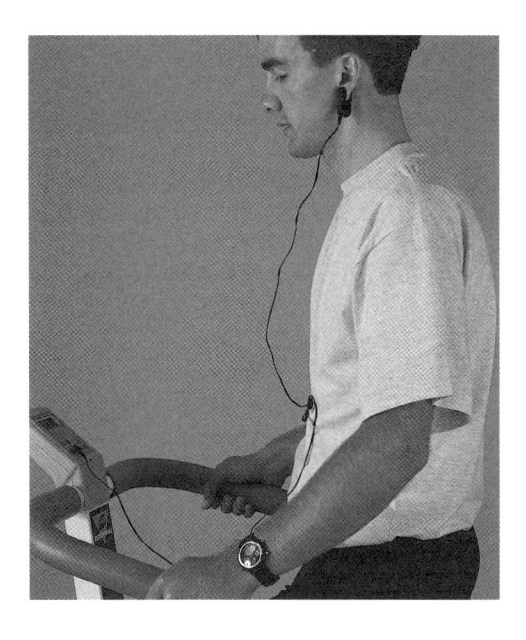

equipment. Currently, reliable heart rate monitors employ electrocardiographic (ECG) techniques that require a chest strap with rubber-covered electrodes and transmit the heart rate to a wrist-worn or handlebar mount unit via telemetry. Several clinical studies have shown that when an athlete is outfitted with both a monitor and a hard-wire ECG unit, there was no significant difference between heart rate recordings.

Elite and world-class athletes and teams have used this technology in everyday training over the last decade for events in cycling, cross-country skiing, running and many other sports. Andy Hampsten and Lance Armstrong are two of the top athletes who have experienced the benefits of training with a heart rate monitor. By using the monitor, a cyclist can take the guesswork out of training. It is useful for reaching top racing form, as an aid for maintaining fitness and for comparing your aerobic conditioning while using different pieces of training equipment.

Finding Your Training Zone

Once you have learned how to monitor your heart rate, your heart's optimum training zone is easy to calculate. But first you must determine your maximum heart rate (max HR). It can be determined during a stress test. However, as a general rule of thumb, your max HR can be estimated by subtracting your age from 220. For example, a 30 year-old would have a max HR of 190 (220 minus 30 equals 190).

You do not train at your max HR. Rather, you set a target zone within a safe heart rate range. For example, if you decide to workout at 70 to 80% of your max HR, and your age is 40 years then your "target heart rate zone" would be 126 to 144 bpm.

220-40 = 180 x 0.70 = 126 bpm

180 x 0.80 = 144 bpm

As with strength training, which has different phases to obtain different results, aerobic training has different training zones. Each zone has its benefits and results. There are three primary heart rate training zones. They are fat-burning, target heart rate and anaerobic zones.

Fat Burning Zone

The fat-burning zone derives its name from the intensity of exercise, which is moderate enough to require your body to use fat as the primary fuel source. Exercise at 50 to 65% of your max HR to achieve this level of intensity. Subtract your age from 220 (your estimated max HR) and multiply by 0.50 and 0.65. The results are the lower and upper heart rate limits of this zone. While you workout in this and the other zones, your heart rate should fall somewhere between these two figures. People just starting an exercise program, or who want to lose weight, should concentrate on maintaining their heart rate in this zone for 20 to 30 minutes per day, 3 to 5 days per week.

Target Heart Rate Zone

The second zone, known as the "aerobic exercise zone," is also shown on many charts as the "target heart rate zone." In this zone you should exercise at 60 to 85% of your max HR. Training in this zone helps you build aerobic endurance and constructs a base upon which you can progressively add more demanding workouts as your cardiovascular fitness increases. Below you will see an example of an aerobic workout in the target heart rate zone for a 40 year old person.

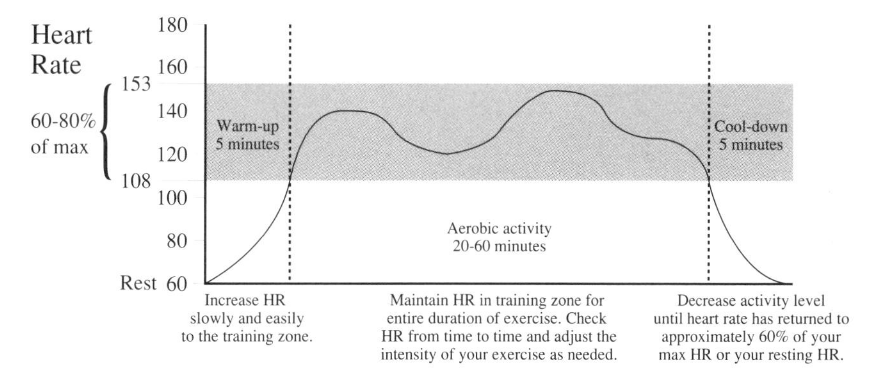

Anaerobic Zone

A higher level of training can help increase both your speed and tolerance for the buildup of lactic acid. This type of workout (from 85 to 100% of max HR), consisting of short hard sprints or repeated hill-running, is referred to as anaerobic training or interval training. Below is an example of the heart rate response during interval training for a 40 year old person.

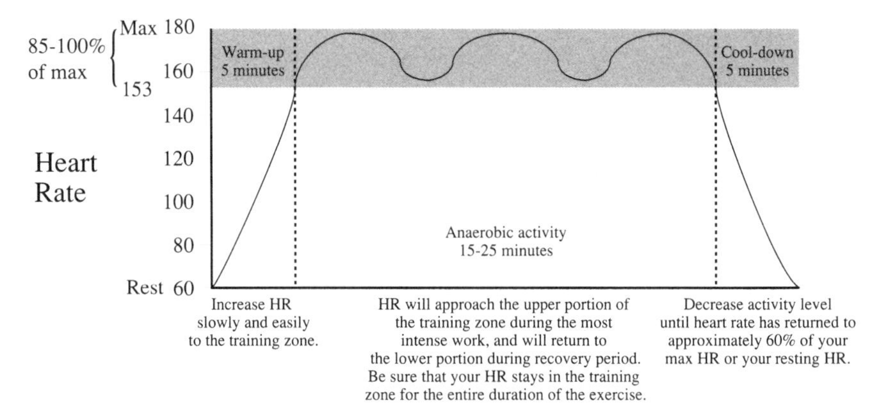

Varied training in all three of these zones will increase your level of fitness, improve your performance, and add more energy to your life. For more detailed information on heart rate training, we recommend that you read The Heart Rate Monitor Book, by Sally Edwards or Cycling Health and Physiology by Ed Burke. Below is a table outlining these three training zones.

Heart Rate Training Zones:		
Zone Type	*% of max*	*Benefit*
Fat Burning	*50 to 60*	*low level intensity - weight control*
Target HR	*65 to 85*	*builds aerobic endurance*
Anaerobic	*85 to 100*	*builds power - speed*

Exercise and Caloric Cost

Many of us are interested in the benefits of cardiorespiratory fitness as well as the amount of calories we burn during our exercise session. When exercising at a higher intensity, and in activities that incorporate larger muscle groups, you will be burning more calories. Besides monitoring your heart rate to avoid over or under-working, it also can assist you in your weight control efforts. For example, a higher heart rate means higher metabolism, and higher metabolism means greater weight loss.

Your daily caloric balance will determine whether you will gain, lose or maintain weight from day-to-day. It is a known physiological fact that one pound of fat is equal to 3500 kcal (more commonly known as Calorie) of energy. Caloric balance refers to the difference between the calories you take in from food eaten and caloric expenditure or the amount of energy you put out in daily activities, work or exercise.

The Performance HRS-30 Rower and ISS-30 Stepper electronic monitors both have caloric counters. Using these, you will be able to record a major component of any weight loss, gain or maintenance program.

Monitoring your calories expended during an aerobic workout can assist you in maintenance, loss or gain of body weight. But, besides the obvious weight control issue, counting calories can also be an effective way to motivate you during your workout.

If you are interested in losing weight, the following guidelines may be helpful when engaging in a program that combines exercise and caloric restriction:

- Make sure you are consuming at least 1,200 kcal per day while dieting. You need to consume this minimum amount of calories for everyday body maintenance and health functions. At this caloric intake level, most nutritionists recommend a vitamin and mineral pill as a supplement, especially for women.
- You should not lose more than two pounds per week on a diet. Therefore, you should not exceed more than a 500 to 1,000 kcal per day negative caloric balance, which is a combination of both caloric restriction and exercise. This combination will result in a gradual weight loss, without a loss of lean body weight (muscle).
- Include an exercise program that provides at least 300 kcal or more of activity per day and at least 1000 to 2000 kcal per week. This is best accomplished with exercise of low intensity (in the 50 to 60% max HR range) and for a longer duration. Low intensity exercise encourages your body to burn more fat. Examples of fat burning exercises are riding or stepping at 55% of your maximum heart rate for 30 minutes or longer.
- Non-weight-bearing activities such as stationary cycling, rowing and stepping may be considered for those who suffer from orthopedic or arthritic problems, and for those who may be obese.
- Include use of behavior modification techniques to identify and eliminate self-defeating dieting and eating habits.
- Finally, and most important, consult a physician before dieting.

Training Tips

To get the maximum benefit out of every workout, you should begin with a short warm-up that lasts a few minutes. Spinning in a small gear, walking on the stepper at a low to moderate resistance, rowing lightly for a few minutes are all examples of a good warm-up. This will prepare you for the work ahead on the rower, stepper or bike by gradually increasing your heart rate and increasing the blood flow to the muscles. Your warm-up should also include some stretching.

Once you have warmed up, start your workout, making sure that you stay within the "target zone" you have selected for that particular workout. If you have not exercised in a few years or are a "weekend warrior," you should stay near the low heart rate intensities of 50 to 60% of max for a target zone. As your fitness increases, you can increase the intensity of your workout and/or extend its duration.

After 20 to 60 minutes of exercise, take a few minutes to cool-down. This is important because it gives your heart and muscles a gradual chance to recover. Incorporate some stretching after your exercise session to aid in recovery.

The following chart is an example of an exercise schedule for one week:

Day	Type	Workout	Notes
Monday	Strength Aerobic	3 sets of 15 reps 20 minutes on trainer	easy day; 40-65% max HR
Tuesday	Aerobic	20 minutes on rower 20 minutes on trainer	easy day; 40-65% of max HR
Wednesday	Strength	3 sets of 15 reps	
Thursday	Aerobic & Anaerobic	50 minutes on trainer with 15/20/15 workout	hard day; 60-85% max HR 20 min; 4 intervals of 2 min hard and 3 min easy 15 min; 50-85% max HR
Saturday		Day off	
Sunday	Aerobic	20 minutes on rower and an hour walk	60-85%max HR

Summary

Vigorous exercise stresses the body allowing it to adapt and improve. The body responds to this stress with certain predictable and identifiable changes in its physical and psychological make up. This phenomenon of stress adaptation is called "the training effect" and is the basis of any successful fitness program.

While you can't demand a guarantee that exercise will add years to your life, you can expect it to improve quality of life. But to improve the quality of your life your training must be consistent, practiced year round and of adequate intensity to stress your cardiovascular system.

Chapter 5 Rowing and Stepping

Rowing Indoors

Successful performance in cycling requires a combination of muscular strength, power and endurance. Improving your cycling requires training on your bike. However, winter conditions usually leave indoor training as the most viable option for maintaining your aerobic fitness level.

If you are looking for an indoor aerobic workout to complement your weight training, a rowing machine can provide a tremendous challenge. Why would a cyclist want to row? It is a great all-around exercise: It strengthens the back, shoulders and arms as well as the buttocks, legs and abdomen. Also, as with cycling, rowing is a non-weight bearing activity, which prevents the pounding that can be experienced in running.

Contrary to popular belief, you do not need arms like Popeye the Sailor man to row. The rowing motion is initiated by a powerful leg drive, followed by the use of the back and finally, the arms and shoulders. The majority of power in the stroke, however, comes from the legs.

The Performance HRS-30 Rowing Machine has dual independent "oars", foot pedals, gas-assisted resistance cylinders and a padded seat that rides on the center rail. Resistance is changed by adjusting the setting from 1 (easy) to 5 (hard) on the "oars." The electronic monitor will give you information on the number of strokes completed, estimate of calories burned and duration of exercise.

Use the stroke rate counter to monitor the number of strokes you take in a particular interval or workout. You can also use the stroke counter to give you an idea of your rate of strokes per minute. This is similar to cadence while cycling.

Getting started with your rowing program should be handled like any other aerobic exercise. Always incorporate warm-up and cool-down periods into your workout, and do some stretching before and after you use the machine. One word of caution - lower back problems can develop in inexperienced rowers. A painful lower back is usually the result of setting the tension too high and using poor form. Once you have learned the technique, you can slowly increase the resistance.

The Stroke

One common mistake is to try to pull up and back with the shoulders at the start of the stroke. Instead, you should keep your shoulders even and level throughout the motion. "Shooting your tail," or allowing the seat to fly backward under the force of your leg-push, while simultaneously leaning forward, wastes a great deal of power and puts stress on your lower back.

There are three parts to the basic stroke:

1. With your upper body leaning slightly forward, move forward on the seat, drawing your knees up to your chest. Your head should be up, arms straight and your back firm..

2. Push back on the foot pedals, exhaling as you pull. When your legs are fully extended, continue the stroke by leaning slightly backward drawing the “oars” to your abdomen or lower chest.

3. Come forward by rolling the palms of your hands downward on the “oars” grips. Then push forward with your palms and wrists. This movement works the muscles in your forearms.

Workouts

Most of us do not experience a great deal of rowing in our daily life so it is extremely important to start gradually. Keep the resistance setting low at first. Beginners might start with 10 to 15 minute sessions that alternate two minutes of rowing with 30 seconds of rest, or aim for about 12 strokes per minute. As you get stronger, increase the duration and resistance gradually, with the goal of about 20 to 25 strokes per minute.

When the rowing action starts to feel routine, you can vary the workout by adding sprints and intervals to your program. During sprints and interval training you will stress your anaerobic energy system. The variety in your training schedule is essential and will improve your overall performance on the rower.

Here are some ways to add power to your workouts:

- Try pulling harder for 10 strokes once every 2 to 3 minutes.
- Alternate three, 5 to 6-minute periods of harder rowing with three, 3-minute periods of easy rowing. More advanced rowers can increase the time and intensity of their workouts.
- Alternate 1 minute of hard sprinting and 1 minute of easy rowing for a total of 20 minutes.
- Lengthen the periods of rest and make the sprints more intense: ex: 90 seconds to 2 minutes all-out, followed by 3 minutes of easy rowing.
- To lose weight, row at an easy-to-moderate intensity for longer periods of time.
- Design workouts similar to those listed in the Indoor Trainer Chapter (Chapter 6).

Injury Prevention

To prevent injury on the rowing machine, follow these guidelines:

- Use your legs, arms and shoulders to do the work and to avoid straining your back.
- Don't start the backward motion with your back. Start with you legs, then gradually use your back, using your extending legs for leverage.
- Make sure your shoulders stay even and level, and don't twist your torso.
- Concentrate on a smooth, economical motion that engages the muscles without undue stress or strain.
- Position your exercise equipment in the coolest part of your house. A room that is comfortable for lounging may seem like a sauna while you are rowing. Temperature in the low 60's is best.

Stair Climbing

Although many people complain about how many flights of stairs they have to climb, some cyclists actually have begun to brag about it. Many fitness researchers are discovering that stair climbing is not only an excellent aerobic conditioner, but provides conditioning for a variety of muscles used in cycling. It is great exercise for the buttocks, hamstrings and quadriceps - the key cycling muscles.

The Performance ISS-30 stair climber utilizes adjustable hydraulic cylinders that give you a smooth and reliable stepping motion.

The Step

Whatever stepper you use, follow these suggestions for correct form:

- Lean you body slightly forward. Your stance should be as if you were walking up a staircase.
- Look straight ahead, into a mirror if possible. This will help you maintain good form throughout the workout.
- Place you feet on the pads about hip-width apart. Your hips should not swing excessively.
- Begin with short strides. If you go into long strides immediately, you may pull a groin muscle or strain you lower back.
- Use the handrails for balance only. The weight has to be totally on your legs to get the maximum benefit.
- Make sure your knees move forward, keeping your weight over your toes. If you place your foot in front of your knee and then try to lift up on that foot, you may strain your knee.

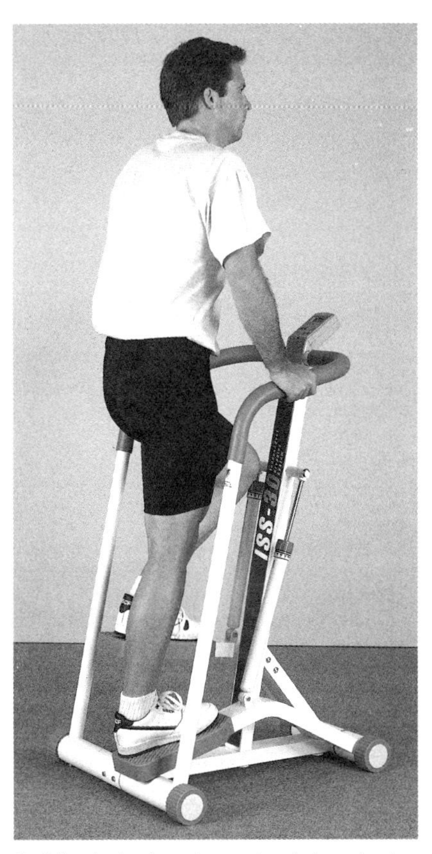

Carl Sundquist, four-time national champion in individual pursuit and 1992 Barcelona Olympian.

1. To work the buttocks muscles, take higher and deeper steps. To work the abdominals, take shorter steps, keeping your feet a little forward of your upper body. You can also work the buttocks and hamstrings (back of thighs) by placing more weight over your heels (step flat-footed).

2. By placing more weight on your toes, you will stress the quadriceps (front of thighs) and calves.

3. Mix quick, short steps with full steps. Short steps work the quadriceps and calves; longer, full steps affect the buttocks and hamstrings.

4. To improve your ability to ride your bike out of the saddle, or to replicate mountain bike riding, train each leg independently. Working at a moderate pace on the stair climber, press harder with the right leg for 25 to 30 repetitions, while pressing lightly with the left leg. Next, focus on the other side.

5. How often have you felt out of balance while trying to apply pressure to the pedals while on a mountain bike? To improve your recovery, play catch with someone while you are stepping, as illustrated below.

6. If you cannot work out with a partner, turn around and walk backwards on the stair climber. This will help you work on your balance. Step with your whole foot (flat-footed) to work the buttocks muscles, the power muscles of cycling.

7. If you want to train your anaerobic energy system, work at a medium pace. Manually increase to a high level of intensity for 30 to 60 seconds, then return to a moderate level.

8. The following is a description of the high/low workout. This endurance workout will vary your stepping technique and emphasize different muscle groups.

- Warm-up at an easy pace for 5 minutes.
- For 5 minutes, pick up your speed a bit and take slightly deeper steps.
- For 5 minutes, take deeper steps (this works the buttocks even more).
- For the next 5 minutes, step with your toes to work the calf muscles and quadriceps.
- For 3 to 5 minutes, go all out increasing your stepping rate and resistance.

- Recover for 3 to 5 minutes at a slow to moderate rate and reduce the resistance.
- For 5 minutes take deep steps with your toes.
- Cool-down for 5 minutes at an easier resistance.

9. Follow the suggestions given in the Indoor Trainer Chapter (Chapter 5) for suggestions on designing additional workouts.

- Make sure the foot pads are not slippery.

Injury Prevention

- Beginners should start with short steps and advance gradually to longer steps. Be careful not to over-strain your groin muscle (upper inner thighs) and lower back.
- Place the stair climber in the coolest part of the house. A room that is comfortable for lounging may seem like a sauna while you are climbing. Temperatures in the low 60's are best.

Unlike cycling and running, a rower works all of your major muscle groups.

Summary

While you simulate the motion of rowing a boat through water, your legs, upper body and mid-section work together against the resistance.

Using a stationary rowing machine is also a great way to expend calories as you slide your way to fitness. Depending on your skill and workout intensity, you burn between 7 and 25 calories per minute. Rowing almost equals cross country skiing for calorie consumption and aerobic conditioning.

Using the correct resistance level is the key to maintaining proper form on stair climbing machines. Too much resistance leads to the most common mistakes: supporting your weight on the handrails and flexing forward at the waist. Locking your elbows to support your body weight leads to less work for your cardiorespiratory system. Use the handrails for balance and assume an upright "neutral" stance with the shoulders, hips, knees and ankles aligned.

The manual settings on the Performance stair climber–unlike pre-programmed settings on other models–give you complete control of intensity, allowing you to establish a base of cardiovascular fitness and learn proper form.

Chapter 6 Spinning Your Wheels Indoors

The biggest problems with winter cycling are early darkness and foul weather. For most of us who must juggle training with very busy schedules, indoor cycling on a wind or magnetic trainer becomes the only real choice. Before you complain about indoor cycling as an unexciting alternative to "real" cycling, note that there are specific benefits worth considering. The controlled environment of a trainer allows you to isolate and concentrate on specific areas of cycling fitness and technique.

Performance offers both rollers and stationary trainers for indoor training. However, other similar units can be used for the workout routines described.

Carl Sundquist, four-time national champion in individual pursuit and 1992 Barcelona Olympian.

Rollers

Rollers consist of three round cylinders mounted on bearings and fixed to a frame. A belt connects one of the rear cylinders to the front cylinder to keep the front wheel spinning at the same speed. Rollers sharpen your bike-handling skills because you must rely on skillful steering and balance. They teach you to work on smooth, fast spinning, but offer very little resistance, unless you add a fan or magnetic unit for increased resistance. It may take many attempts to be able to feel relaxed and confident on your rollers. Once you are past the initial learning stages, the bike-handling skills you obtain will make you a more confident and successful cyclist.

Carl Sundquist, four-time national champion in individual pursuit and 1992 Barcelona Olympian.

Wind vs. Magnetic Trainers

Wind trainers have two fan units with slotted blades that churn the air. Magnetic trainers have powerful magnets and a non-conductive disk that produces resistance and dissipates energy as heat. Performance mag trainers have six resistance settings (low to high) that are controlled by a bar-mounted lever.

A wind trainer's greatest advantage for indoor training is that it closely mimics the resistance you experience on the road, increasing resistance exponentially. If you were to increase your speed on the wind-load simulator from 15 to 30 mph, you would need to increase your power output by a factor of about 8 times to reach 30 mph. The disadvantages of wind trainers are the noise generated by the fans and the lack of resistance adjustment.

Mag resistance units increase resistance in direct proportion to speed, a feature less realistic than wind-load simulators. But mag units do provide enough drag to elevate your heart rate. The Performance Variable Resistance Magnetic units incorporate a small, precisely weighted flywheel which creates a slight "coasting" sensation. This helps you pedal through the dead spots in your pedal stroke for a more realistic road feel. Advantages of mag trainers over wind trainers include reduced noise levels and the ability to vary resistance.

Wind Resistance Unit

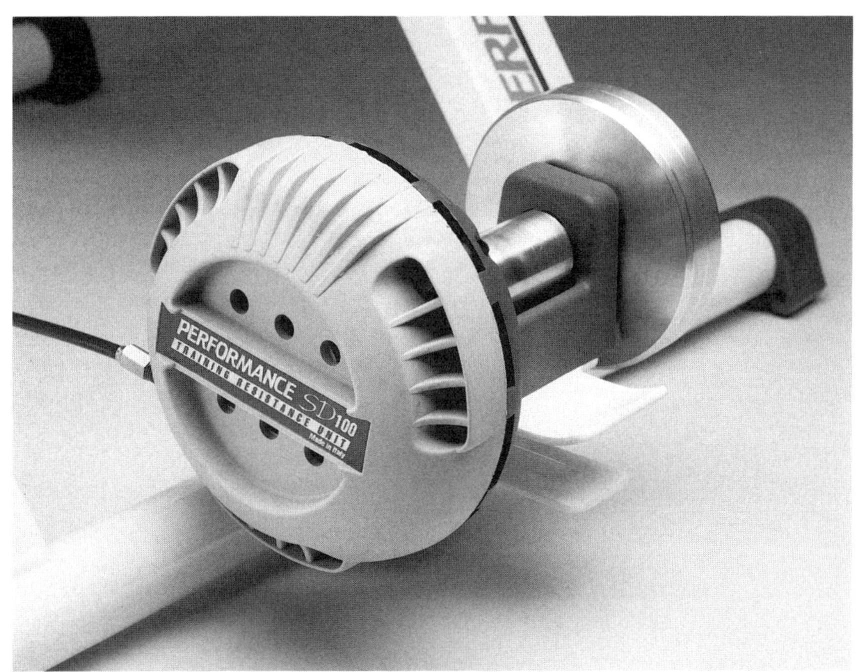

Magnetic Resistance Unit

Spinning

Working out on an indoor trainer can provide opportunities to see rapid improvements in riding technique. The isolated environment of indoor training allows you to concentrate on specific skills without distraction. Spinning, the ability to maintain a high cadence with a continuous application of power, can be improved by simply listening to the trainer's noise. If you hear a steady "whoosh" only on the down stroke, you are not pedaling properly. Concentrate on pedaling in circles. You will find that this helps you begin the power stroke earlier at the top, and pulls your foot across the bottom of the stroke. After a while you will develop a longer and smoother application of power throughout the entire pedal stroke.

Workouts

As with all exercise, remember to spend a few minutes warming-up and cooling-down. Cycling outdoors is quite different than cycling indoors where you don't have the wind to keep you cool. Therefore, we recommend the use of a fan. Otherwise, within 5 minutes, you'll be overheated. Also, fill your water bottle before the start of your workout, and consider riding in the coolest part of the house.

To make your workouts more enjoyable, be creative. Make a couple of training tapes of your favorite songs (preferably something with a strong beat) and put on your headphones when you start to pedal. Use a bike computer to monitor your progress, keeping a log of times, distance and speed, or use a heart rate monitor to track your workout level. By making your training fun, you can avoid burnout and improve your cycling skills.

Chris Carmichael, Director of Athlete Development for the U.S. Cycling Federation, recommends spending no more than 2 hours per day on the trainer. He has seen many inexperienced riders who have spent a great deal of time on stationary trainers, come into the season flying, then fade in June and July.

For general conditioning, find a resistance and gear combination that elevates your heart-rate into your training zone. After your warm-up, raise your rpms to the 85 to 95 range with your heart-rate at no more than 85 % of your maximum.

For climbing strength, and to become accustomed to pushing larger gears, put the bike into a gear (or use a mag trainer and increase the resistance) that forces you to drop your cadence about 15 rpms. Maintain this cadence for several minutes and repeat several times during a training session.

For speed work and to work on your anaerobic capacity, intervals on a trainer are just the answer. There are many types of interval programs that you can structure on the trainer, similar to those you use on the road. The key is to remember not to overwork during this time of the season.

A final tip: ride your trainer only every other day. Otherwise, you are likely to get stale. On days that you don't ride, get your aerobic workout by rowing or stepping. You can row or lift weights the same day you ride.

Here are examples of several workouts that can be used on bicycle trainers. Variations of these workouts can also be used on steppers and rowers.

1. Start with a 10 minute hard effort followed by 2 minutes of easy spinning for recovery. The next interval should be 8 minutes of hard, then 2 minutes of easy effort. Each hard interval decreases by 2 minutes but increases slightly in intensity. The easy 2 minutes remains the same. The workout ends when you reach 2 hard minutes and 2 easy minutes.

2. Ride progressively harder gears. Start in a relatively low gear and ride in it for 1 to 2 minutes, then shift to the next higher gear, etc. (keeping the same cadence throughout exercise). When you are finished in the highest gear you plan to ride, ride back "down the ladder." Usually, riding up 4 to 5 gears is sufficient for a good workout.

3. There are dozens of variations on the above workout. Hard gear, easy gear, back to hard, up 2, down 1, etc. You can also vary the cadence, increasing it to 110 to 120 rpm for a minute or so but always keeping it above 80 rpm.

4. To develop speed, throw in some intervals: 10 to 12 all-out 15-second pedaling sprints alternating with 45 seconds of easy pedaling.

5. To develop power, try 3 to 6 repetitions of 3 minutes at 90 rpm in a big gear, with 3 minutes of low gear spinning between efforts.

6. Here's a good workout when you want to do an endurance ride at a specific "heart rate zone." For example, if you want to workout between 75 and 80% of your max HR for a good aerobic workout use the following workout:

• Warm-up for about 5 minutes, starting with low-to-moderate gears, gradually raising your rpms or gearing until your heart rate is 75% of your maximum.

• For the next 30 minutes keep your heart rate within 75 to 80% of the max target heart-rate zone. That's the range you calculated before getting on the bike. The challenge of this workout is to keep your heart-rate there. If it falls below or rises above this zone, increase or decrease your effort accordingly.

• Cool-down for 5 to 10 minutes until your heart-rate has returned below 110 to 120 beats-per-minute.

7. Another exercise that has drastic results is one-legged cycling on a wind load or mag trainer. Most of us are not symmetrical in our application of power to the pedals; we favor one leg by exerting more force on the pedal with this leg. The result is asymmetrical pedaling that leads to a loss of power.

- Place one foot on a 16-inch box, and with the other leg try your best to pedal smooth circles for 5 to 10 minutes. Without the inertial support of the other leg, you will find that this exercise improves your ability to apply power over a larger portion of the crank circle.
- After several weeks of working both legs, slip the trainer into a very low gear and, while using both legs, attempt to pedal with smooth power application. This is what professional cyclist refer to as pedaling with "suppleness."

Carl Sundquist, four-time national champion in individual pursuit and 1992 Barcelona Olympian.

Injury Prevention

- When first learning to ride rollers, mount your bike with the aid of a wall or chair. This will help you maintain your balance.
- On rollers, the more momentum you can give your wheels, the more stable the bicycle will be, just like on the road, but more critical here.
- Keep a fan blowing on you if you are riding in a warm room, and drink fluids as if you were riding outdoors.
- Whether on rollers, wind or mag trainer, pedal smoothly and do not bounce excessively on the bicycle. Concentrate on smooth pedaling to avoid putting too much stress on your knees.
- Keep small children away from moving parts, so fingers do not become caught in fan blades, rubber bands or spinning wheels.

Summary

Whether you live in frigid Vermont or rain-soaked Seattle, the best way to avoid losing you cycling edge during the cold winter months is to use the snowbound cyclist's best friend - an indoor trainer. This ingenious device, which simulates the same kind of resistance you normally encounter outdoors, gives you a great workout, and can also help maintain, or even improve your cycling form until you hit the road again.

A good training program includes a healthy mix of workouts. Try the hard/easy approach, alternating days of steady state riding with power or sprint sessions. If you feel tired on a day when you are scheduled for a hard interval session, relax and spin for 30 to 60 minutes. You'll still have plenty of time during the rest of the winter to catch up on your training.

Chapter 7 Stretching

Good physical performance is based on strength, power and endurance. But there is still another important component to this formula that many cyclists tend to overlook - flexibility. Increased flexibility can be achieved by adding stretching to your fitness program. Stretching is also highly recommended by the American College of Sports Medicine.

As you ride, row, step or strength-train on resistance equipment, your muscles become stronger, but also tighter. You may experience tightness and pain in the lower back, hamstrings or shoulders. This is a warning sign that you are experiencing a gradual loss of muscle elasticity and a decrease in joint flexibility. Stretching, which requires no special skill, can relieve this condition, aid recovery and help prevent soreness.

Stretching before your workout will help circulate more blood through your muscles and prepare them for the hard work to come. Stretching between exercises (or when you change pieces of equipment) will help relieve muscle tension and may help postpone fatigue. Stretching after your workout, will help you cool-down and may prevent some soreness.

The Stretch

A long, sustained stretch - called a static stretch - is a far superior method of stretching your muscles and surrounding connective tissue than bouncing or ballistic stretching. An easy static stretch should be done without any feeling of pain that can be associated with other types of stretching techniques.

Get used to feeling an "easy" stretch, a stretch that feels good, for 15-30 seconds. The longer you maintain an easy stretch, the more tension you will relieve in the muscles you stretch. Stretching correctly improves your flexibility, which is an essential component of your overall fitness. As with strength and aerobic training, it is essential not to shock your muscles by performing a strenuous stretch with a "cold" muscle. Warm up your muscles with a low intensity exercise such as jogging in place or knee lifts and arm circles. A warm muscle is less likely to be injured and is easier to stretch.

Lower back pain is also a common injury and can be aggravated if stretching is performed incorrectly. To protect your lower back it is important to make sure it does not arch excessively. Keep your lower back as flat as possible, even if it slightly reduces the amount of stretch

Stretch Exercises

To help fit stretching into your busy off-season schedule, we have included a 10-minute program that can be done before, after or even during your workout. These same stretches can also be used during the cycling season to aid with stiffness you may experience after a long, hard ride. The following stretches, from Stretching by Bob Anderson, are highly recommended.

Elongation

- Straighten out your arms and legs. Point your fingers and toes as you stretch as far as you can. Stretch and then relax. Hold for five seconds. This is a good stretch for the entire body

Achilles and Calf Stretch

- The back leg should start out straight with the foot flat and pointing straight ahead. Slightly bend the back knee, still keeping the foot flat. This gives you a much lower stretch, which is also good for maintaining or regaining ankle flexibility. Hold 15 seconds each leg. This area needs only a slight feeling of stretch.

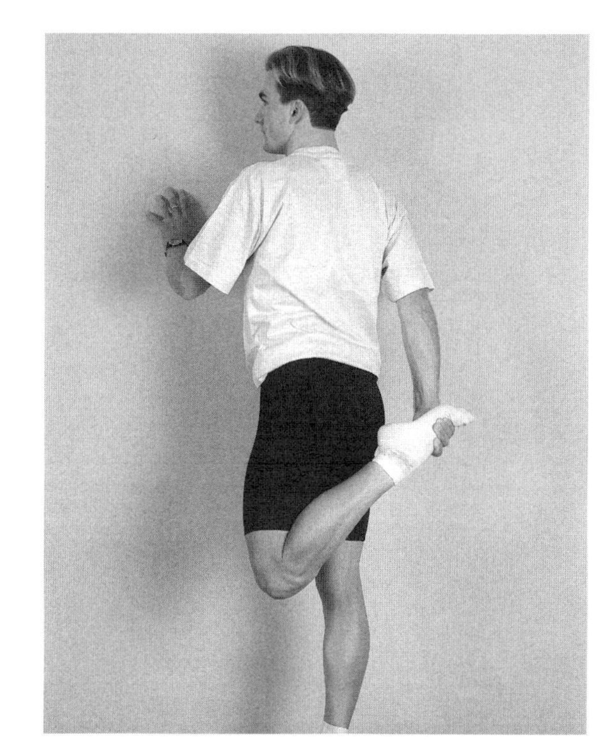

Standing Quads

- Hold top of left foot (from inside of foot) with right hand and gently pull, heel moving toward buttocks. Do both legs.

Shoulder Shrug

- Raise the top of your shoulders toward your ears until you feel slight tension in your neck and shoulders. Hold this feeling of tension for three to five seconds, then relax your shoulders downward into their normal position, Do this two to three times. Good to use at the first signs of tightness or tension in the shoulder and neck area.

Pull Elbow Across

- To stretch your shoulder and middle of upper back, gently pull your elbow across your chest toward your opposite shoulder. Hold stretch for 10 seconds. Do both arms.

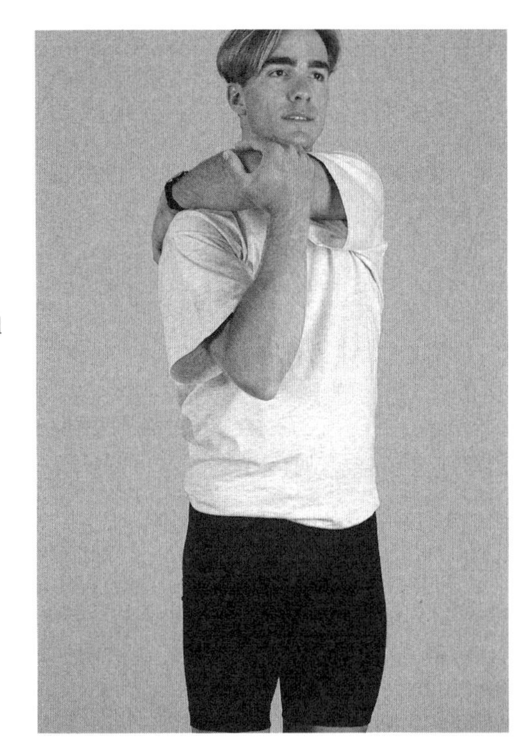

Williams Flex Stretch

- Straighten both legs and relax, then pull your left leg toward your chest. For this stretch keep the back of your head on the mat, if possible, but do not strain. Repeat with your right leg.

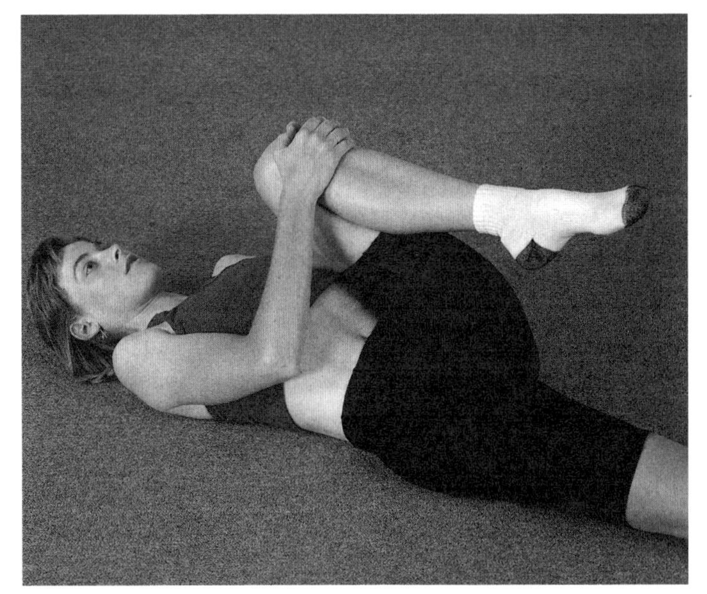

Fence Pull

- Place both hands shoulder width apart on a ledge (the top of a refrigerator or fence is good) and let your upper body drop down as you keep your knees slightly bent (one inch). Your hips should be directly above your feet. To change the area of the stretch, bend your knees just a bit more and/or place your hands at different heights. This will take some of the kinks out of a tired upper back.

Sitting Groin

- Put the soles of your feet together with your heels a comfortable distance from your groin., Put your hands around your feet and slowly pull yourself forward until you feel an easy stretch in the groin. Make your movement forward by bending from the hips and not from the shoulders. If possible, keep your elbows on the outside of your lower legs.

Sprinters Stretch

- Move one leg forward until the knee of the forward leg is directly over the ankle. Your other knee should be resting on the floor. Now, without changing the position of the knee on the floor or the forward foot, lower the front of your hip downward to create an easy stretch. This will help relieve tension in the lower back.

Turn Head to Side

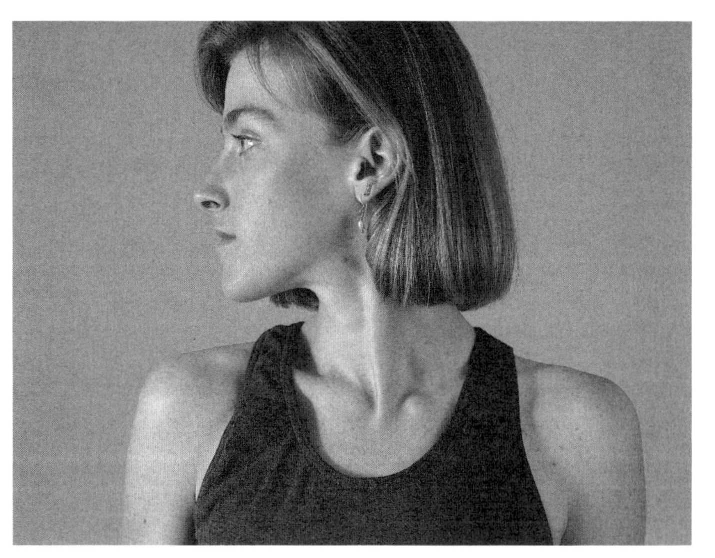

- From a stable, aligned sitting position, turn your chin toward your left shoulder to create a stretch on the right side of your neck. Hold correct stretch tensions for 10 to 20 seconds. Do each side twice.

Summary

It is easy to forego stretching, but it is as important to your overall fitness as your strength and aerobic conditioning. Stretching can also serve as relaxation time, which we tend to get too little of in our busy schedules, yet is so important for our overall health.

It should only take a few minutes to stretch properly before and after you exercise. This small amount of time can keep injuries and tightness to a minimum. As you stretch, you learn about your body and how it moves and feels. And you learn how to take care of your body to prevent injury and excess tension. Stretching is a great form of physical education.

We wish you the best of luck with your cross-training program. Your investment in Performance home fitness equipment will prepare you for upcoming events and help you reach your physical potential. Don't feel too guilty about not being on your bike as much during the off-season. Other types of aerobic activities will keep you in top form and will prevent you from getting stale. Include some resistance training exercises to improve your strength, power and endurance.

This combination of aerobic exercise with strength training is referred to as "balanced fitness." It will make you healthier, increase your productivity and, perhaps most important, can make you a better cyclist. The benefits that balanced fitness provide cannot be denied and, once discovered, cannot be ignored.

Enjoy your Performance fitness equipment and we will see you on the road in the spring.

Suggested Reading

Anderson, Bob. Stretching. Shelter Publications, Inc., Solinas, CA, 1980.

Burke, Edmund. Health and Physiology of Cycling. Vitesse Press, Brattleboro, VT, 1992.

Edwards, Sally. The Heart Rate Monitor Book. POLAR/CIC, Port Washington, NY, 1992.

Institute for Aerobics Research. The Strength Connection. Institute for Aerobics Research, Dallas, TX, 1990.

Klavora, Peter. Circuit Training For All Sports. Sports Books Publishers, Toronto, Canada, 1992.

Kuntzlemen, Charles. Rowing Machine Workouts. Contemporary Books, Inc. Chicago, IL, 1985.

Matheny, Fred and Stephen Grabe. Weight Training for Cyclists. Velo-news, Brattleboro, VT, 1986.

The National Exercise for Life Institute. The New Fitness Formula of the 90's. The National Exercise for Life Institute, Excelsior, MN, 1990.

Videotape:
Newton, Harvey. Strength Training for Cyclists. Newton Sports, PO Box 2595, Colorado Springs, CO, 80910-2595